To please her fiancé, Jana had come to Devil's View, near Capetown, to try and find some vital information. But she could only succeed in her search if she took the job of secretary to the enigmatic Clint Dubois. It was clear that Clint suspected her motives—but was that the only reason she found him so disturbing?

# RETURN TO DEVIL'S VIEW

BY
ROSEMARY CARTER

MILLS & BOON LIMITED
17–19 FOLEY STREET
LONDON W1A 1DR

*First published 1979*
*Australian copyright 1979*
*Philippine copyright 1979*
*This edition 1979*

© Rosemary Carter 1979

ISBN 0 263 73092 1

*Set in Linotype Baskerville 11 on 12½ pt.*

*Made and printed in Great Britain by*
*Richard Clay (The Chaucer Press) Ltd., Bungay, Suffolk*

misjudge Simon and his mother when she imagined they might not understand why it was hard for her to go on with her quest?

Whatever the case, she could do nothing about it now. Perhaps not even today. Not until she had thought of a way in which to make her request seem reasonable. And not until she had found out a little about the people who lived here. It had taken only a glimpse of the estate for Jana to know that she could not baldly confront the owners of Devil's View with a question which they might well consider impertinent.

Her hands released their grip. She was frowning as she walked slowly back to the Mini. But as she turned the car and began to drive slowly back along the way she had travelled her face cleared, and she resolved to forget her mission for a few hours.

Just as the grandeur of Devil's View had not remained in her memory, so the loveliness of the Cape Peninsula had been forgotten. 'The fairest cape in all the world ...' The words Francis Drake had spoken hundreds of years earlier drifted back into Jana's mind as she negotiated the steep bends in the road. Above her rose the wooded slopes of Table Mountain, and to one side, in sharp relief against the sky, was Devil's Peak, the mountain from which the wine estate had taken its name. Below her lay the sprawl of houses which was Cape Town and its suburbs, and beyond that was the sea. Jana wound down her window and took deep breaths of the fresh mountain air, crisp and sharp with the mingled aromas of pine trees and wild flowers, and the sea drew her gaze. It held an invitation which was suddenly irresistible.

At Fish Hoek she stopped the car. Changing into her bikini, she mentally blessed the impulse which had led her to throw it into her suitcase a moment before she and Simon had left for the airport. The bikini was green, and Simon said that when she wore it the colour of her eyes was enhanced. She remembered his disapproval when she had packed it.

'You're not going to be swimming.'

'I might.' She had danced him a smile, and then, because she could not resist teasing him when he looked so serious, she had added, 'You're not scared I'll find myself a boy-friend?'

'Don't be absurd.' His voice had been stiff. 'You're engaged to me. Besides, if you did that it would make nonsense of this whole trip.'

'I was joking with you, darling.' She was remorseful, knowing that she had hurt him. Yet for an instant she could not help wishing that his nature was not quite so serious.

She spread her towel on the sandy beach and sat down, leaning back on her elbows to gaze about her entranced. The little beach had an atmosphere all its own. There was the village of Fish Hoek, a picturesque sprawl at the foot of the mountain, and the fishing boats bobbing at the quayside. A small craft skimmed the water, and as it reached the quay Jana gathered from the good-natured shouting that there had been a good haul of snoek. Fishermen stood on the rocks, and everywhere there were gulls. They flew over the water, darting into the waves, then soaring upwards again.

The tide was coming in as Jana ran to the water. She braced herself to meet the shock of the cold and was astonished at the mildness of the water. For several minutes she let herself enjoy the feel of the waves breaking about her body. Then, seeing a wave begin to rise, she dived into it and began to swim.

A strong swimmer, she had soon passed the loose group of bathers who stood on the sandy sea bottom and waited for the waves to lift them. There was joy in moving through the water, but she knew the folly of going out too far. After a while she stopped swimming, and turned on her back and floated. All thoughts of her mission vanished as she gave herself over to the bliss of the sea. The waves surged and ebbed as they rolled shorewards, gentle waves which lifted and lowered her as they went. She thought she could never tire of the movement.

The water was very blue, and the mist-covered mountain was always in sight. Now and then, when a wave lifted her, she could make out a ship, a vague shape on the horizon, and the head of a swimmer a little further out than she was herself.

Absorbed in her unaccustomed enjoyment of the waves, she did not notice at first that the swell was beginning to move sidewards. It was only when a wave lifted her that she saw, with astonishment, that she was drifting away from the bathing beach.

Turning over, she began to swim shorewards. The fact that she had to fight the sidewards pull did not alarm her; she could swim well enough to know that she could cope.

She hit the whirlpool quite suddenly. One moment she was swimming, and the next she was caught in a swirling patch of water. She tried to fight the swirl, but it was too strong for her. It took her only moments to realise that she could not get out of it.

She did not know that she screamed as her arms and legs flailed the water. The tide was stronger now, and the waves higher. She had never been more helpless.

She did not see the man swim towards her, and when her shoulders were seized in a vice-like grip she let out an exclamation of shock. In a second he had pulled her clear.

It was only later, when Jana had had time to think, that she understood why her rescuer had had no trouble with the swirl himself—the actual extent of the whirlpool had been so limited that he had not been caught in it.

Still holding her, he began to swim shorewards. For a few seconds Jana could feel nothing but relief. Then, as she realized that he thought she still needed help, she tried to pull away. His response was to take a tighter grip on her. She threw back her head and tried to look at him.

'Keep still!' he ground out.

The harshness in his tone took her by surprise.

Shocked, she lay passively in his arms, his body above hers as he took them both through a wave. In the moment when her head had been back, she had caught sight of his eyes. They were dark, wild and fierce, and with an expression of anger which bewildered her. The arms which held her were lean and muscled, and even with the odds of the sea's sidewise pull and Jana's inert body to weigh him down, he was swimming strongly.

Recovered from her fear, Jana found that she was intensely aware of him. There seemed not an inch of his body which was not in contact with hers. She could feel the broad chest against her breasts, the powerful legs sweeping hers as he swam, in a rhythm which seemed effortless. She had never been quite so close to a man before, not even to Simon. There was no reason why she should feel shaken and at the same time intensely alive. The enforced intimacy with this stranger was merely a consequence of the rescue. Nevertheless, she felt as if the breath had been knocked from her lungs, making it difficult for her to breathe.

They came to shallower water, and Jana's rescuer stopped swimming and stood upright. As her feet touched the ground she pulled away from him. At the same moment, his hands dropped to his sides. For the first time she could see more of the man than the wildness of his eyes. He was very tall, even taller than she had imagined. His shoulders were broad, his chest muscled, and beneath the droplets of water his torso gleamed like burnished bronze.

'I want to thank you for . .,' she began, and was interrupted with a savage 'Skip it!'

'I don't understand ...' She stared up at him. The anger she had glimpsed in his eyes a few minutes earlier had deepened. She saw the rigid line of his jaw, and the hard set of his lips. Fear fluttered in her throat.

'I was just trying to thank you,' she managed to whisper.

'An apology would be more in line.' His lips were curved in an arrogant line.

Disbelievingly she stared into eyes that sparkled like flint. 'For being in trouble?' she flung at him, and now she too was angry.

'For swimming out of your depth.' His eyes flicked her with contempt. 'It's inconsideration like yours which makes trouble for lifeguards.'

She had been about to explain about the whirl-pool, but his arrogance made her think better of it. Defiantly she lifted her chin. 'You don't like work-ing for your living?' She did not know what made her say it, except perhaps that his manner had goaded her into it. If the man was a lifeguard he must know of the invisible dangers which lurked in his terrain.

His lips parted in a mocking smile, and she saw the flash of teeth, intensely white against the bronze mask of his face. Black eyes gleamed with a quality she could not define. Malice? Anger? Behind the bravado of her taunt, her pulses quickened as she braced herself for his reply.

She did not get the answer she expected. While they had been talking a wave had begun to rise, a bigger wave than the rest, tall and green and with foam beginning to form at its crest. Eyes wide with terror, Jana stared at the wall of water. In that moment she could not think what to do. She knew only that the great wave would crash on to her and sweep her downwards.

The man's reflexes were quicker than her own. Without a word he seized her, and dived them both headlong through the wave. He was still holding her as the wave crashed beyond them in a furious torrent of surging foam. The worst of the terror had passed. Jana tried to stand, but her legs were so weak that she felt them buckle beneath her.

'Hold it ...' She heard his voice above the roar of the sea. She tried to look at him, to tell him that she was all right, but the words did not come. This was the second time he had saved her, and she felt the need to say something, anything....

As if he guessed her thoughts she heard him say, 'No need to make small-talk.' His tone was jeering, but when she jerked her head back to look at him she saw that his eyes were sombre.

The wave had left a surging swell of water in its wake, and he was still holding her. If he had let her go she might have been dragged along with the torrent. She should be grateful.... But she could only wonder if it was necessary for him to hold her so close that she could feel the tautness of his thighs pressing against her legs, and the strong beat of his heart through the fabric of her bikini.

'You're enjoying this, aren't you?' she accused.

'Of course. What healthy red-blooded male wouldn't?' He grinned suddenly and she caught her breath as he pulled her even closer.

'Don't kiss me!' Heavens! How could she have said such a stupid thing! But it was too late to withdraw the words.

She felt colour flooding her face as his lips curled in derisive amusement. 'So that's what you're angling for?'

'I've just told you I'm not. . . .'

'No?' His eyes were polished flints, and she saw his head bend. She held her breath. Even while she readied herself to fight him, she was wondering how his lips would feel. She could not bear to meet his gaze. Her eyes closed.

A moment passed. Slowly the emerald eyes fluttered open. She darted a quick glance at the cynical face just inches from her own, then her gaze shifted.

'So. . . .' The mocking tone seared her nerve-stream. He paused, but she knew that he would not let her off so lightly. She forced herself to still the trembling in her limbs, no easy matter when she was enveloped by a quite overpowering maleness. 'You don't want me to kiss you.'

It was not phrased in the manner of a question, but she felt obliged to answer it. 'I'm not in the habit of being intimate with strangers,' she said stiffly.

'I won't argue the point.' He laughed, and the

sound was low and sensual. Disbelieving. 'It just so happens that you're safe. Making love to children in distress does not happen to be my scene.'

Anger surged through her, swift and hot and all the more fierce because he had touched a raw spot. It was humiliating that he saw through her denial. Even more humiliating was the knowledge that she had wanted, just for one brief second, to feel his lips. . . . Furiously she tried to wrench an arm from his grip. The urge to slap the arrogant face was instinctive. But he was stronger than she was. As if he sensed her desire, the grip tightened. It became a vice of iron, and as she looked helplessly into the chiselled mask of his face, bronzed and lean and rugged, she saw that his jaw had hardened.

'Shall we make for the beach?' The mildness of his tone was subtle mockery.

The torrent of water had subsided. Jana had control of herself now. Emerald eyes flashed the man a look of defiance as she shook herself free and began to make her way out of the water. She did not need to look sideways to know that he was close beside her. The waves rose and fell, milder waves these, posing no great problem. Harder to cope with was Jana's awareness of the lifeguard. Coupled with his infuriating arrogance was an aura of sensual power and ruthlessness which she had never encountered before.

They were at the water's edge, and she was about to make her way to her towel, when a peremptory hand touched her arm.

'Well?' Involuntarily her gaze went from the long fingers pressing into her flesh to the mocking eyes in the lean face.

'Are you always so prickly?' His glance was sardonic as it studied her, the sparkling green eyes and the defiant set of the lips, then it travelled deliberately downwards to linger in turn on softly rounded breasts, tiny waist and long slender legs. For the first time Jana wished that she had worn a one-piece swimming costume. If the bikini enhanced the colour of her eyes, it was also revealing.

She forced herself to stand still. It was an effort to speak through the sudden attack of breathlessness. 'Prickly?' she managed to demand.

'Very.' His lips curved in amusement and there was an unholy light in the dark eyes. 'And so at variance with the rest of you.' Again, and with studied insolence, his gaze rested on the roundness above the bikini top. 'Parts of you are anything but prickly.'

If Simon was here, would he hit this man very hard? Jana felt for her engagement ring. In Simon's absence she could at least threaten the lifeguard with her fiancé's anger. Then she remembered that she had left the ring in her purse because she had been uncertain whether the salt water would affect the radiance of the diamond. Unbidden came the thought that even if Simon had been here, he would not have fought. And why should he? She was immediately repentant for what seemed a disloyal thought. Simon was slight and sensitive; there was no reason why he should tangle with this muscled hulk of a man. No reason at all. . . . And she wondered what there was about the lifeguard that should have made her think of anything as senselessly Victorian as a duel.

'A warning,' he was saying. 'Remember not to swim out of your depth.'

Perhaps it was his contempt that made it impossible for her to tell him about the whirlpool. She was wondering how best to free her arm from his grip when a feminine voice said, 'Darling, you've met a friend? Won't you introduce me?'

Jana turned. The girl who had come upon them unnoticed, and who now stood close beside the lifeguard, wore a bikini which was even scantier than Jana's, and which revealed her voluptuous curves to breathtaking advantage. Her hair was dark and glossy, but her blue eyes were cold as they studied Jana with undisguised hostility.

'A friend?' The man shrugged, and Jana thought he seemed amused at the mutual sizing-up of the two girls. 'I don't even know her name, Miranda.'

'In the circumstances my name is irrelevant. Thank you for rescuing me. If I may have my arm. . . .' Jana glanced pointedly at the strong fingers which still held her.

'Of course.' His voice was dispassionate as he released her.

'Rescue?' Miranda asked, as Jana made to turn away.

'I was in difficulties,' Jana said briefly, wondering

that a girl who seemed to have everything in the way of looks should feel the need to be so possessive. And of this arrogant man into the bargain.

'Now I've heard everything' The tinkling of the high brittle laugh set Jana's nerves on edge. 'Difficulties in False Bay? Why, the sea here is as calm as a pond.' Another laugh. 'Still, I guess it's a novel approach to get a man's attention.'

Jána forbore the urge to tell Miranda that if a lifeguard was her choice of a boy-friend, she must learn to live with the range of his duties. For a moment she even felt an irrational tinge of sympathy with the girl. It must be hard to trust a man who treated every female he met with an insolent familiarity. Then she saw again the venom in the blue eyes and the sympathy vanished. These two were of a kind—let them have joy of each other.

Under normal circumstances Jana would have thanked the lifeguard for rescuing her, but as she met his gaze, filled with mockery and amusement, she could not bring herself to utter the necessary words. She was one female who would not pander to the vanity of this Don Juan. Thanks were due, but then she had tried to thank him earlier and had been rebuffed. Besides, he had done nothing but his duty. At worst he might think her lacking in courtesy. She would never see him again, so his opinion did not matter. Once she had accomplished her mission at Devil's View she would take the next plane back to Johannesburg. The afternoon on the beach would fade in her memory, so that if she re-membered it at all it would be merely as an inter-lude.

When she had towelled herself dry with a fierce-ness which was not warranted, she spread her towel on the sand and sat down. She meant to look at the sea and the boats and the mountain which towered above the little resort; to drink in the beauty which she did not remember from childhood but had seen only in pictures. Yet, as if drawn by a magnet, her eyes went to the man and the girl walking away from her. They were very close to the water, and an incoming wave curled around their ankles. The girl had her hand on the man's back, and as Jana watched, his arm encircled her shoulders. It was with a determined wrench that Jana jerked her eyes back to a study of her surroundings.

The joy seemed to have vanished from the after-noon, and she knew that it was the lifeguard who was the cause of it. Green eyes stared thoughtfully at the tracery of masts and sails in the fishing-har-bour. It went without saying that he meant nothing to her. She did not know his name; did not want to know it. She never wanted to see him again. Too arrogant, too sure of himself, he was the antithesis of all that she respected in a man. Jana knew the type she was drawn to, a man who was sensitive and gentle and caring, who did not rely on physical qualities to make an impact on a woman. A man like Simon.

Why then had the lifeguard so disturbed her? Unwillingly she had to admit to herself that in the moments when he had held her close to him, when she had been aware of his innate maleness through the pull and swirl of the waves, she had felt an excitement which she had never experienced with Simon, an excitement which was primitive and primaeval. She had wanted him to kiss her—as much as she had sought to deny it, he had been right about that. It was this same excitement which still disturbed her now. She could rationalise all she pleased, she could tell herself that her awareness of the man had been a product of danger and enforced intimacy; yet she knew that in all the months of Simon's courtship she had never felt quite as feminine and as vibrantly alive as when the lifeguard's arms had been around her. The thought troubled her.

Bending to smooth her towel, she saw the bare finger on her left hand. Simon's ring was still in her purse. How horrified he would be if he knew it. And why had she forgotten to put it back on? She shook herself impatiently as she opened the purse and slipped the ring on to her finger. She was being over-imaginative now. There was nothing symbolic in a simple case of forgetfulness.

All at once she was restless. She still saw the loveliness all around her, but she no longer felt a part of it. As she stood up and shook the sand from her towel, she told herself that the encounter in the water had nothing to do with her reasons for wanting to leave the beach. The sunny afternoon was drawing to a close and a cold wind had lifted from the sea and was blowing shorewards. It was time to leave anyway.

# CHAPTER TWO

THE sun was beginning to set as Jana took the mountain road. Simon had given her the name of a hotel in Cape Town which had been recommended to him by one of his business acquaintances, the man who had lent Jana the Mini. One look at the hotel from the outside and Jana had known it was not for her. Located in the centre of the city, it had an air of staid propriety which did not appeal to her. Even though she would be here only a few days, the loveliness of the Peninsula had infected her with a holiday feeling. She decided to find a smaller hotel, preferably out of the city.

A chance remark had led her to the inn high on the slopes of the mountain, and her spirits rose as she approached it. The low white-painted house with its thatched roof and classic Cape Dutch gable had evidently been a private home once. Little of its essential character had been changed when it became an inn. Nestling in a fold of the mountain, it was surrounded by trees. There were pines and firs and the silver trees which grew in such profusion on Table Mountain. In the grounds no attempt had been made to cultivate flowers. There were no neat beds and clipped edges; the garden relied on the indigenous plants of the Cape for its colour and

character. Amidst the trees she saw aloes and proteas in merging shades of red and mauve and orange,
and though it was smaller and less grand, there was
something about this garden which made her think
of the grounds she had glimpsed at Devil's View.

Before dinner she sat for a while in the lounge
with its view over the sea, and tried to concentrate
on the mission which had brought her to the Cape.
For hours she had not thought about it at all; the
encounter on the beach had erased all else from
her mind. Involuntarily the image of her rescuer
appeared before her. She closed her eyes and for a
moment she felt again the broad chest against hers,
the taut-muscled thighs moving against her legs in
disciplined strokes.

Angrily her eyes snapped open. She would *not*
think about the lifeguard, who had done no more
than was required of him. She had the feeling that
by thinking of him she was being disloyal to Simon,
perhaps because she had allowed herself to make
a comparison between her gentle fiancé and that
arrogant hulk of a man.... And that was no cause
for her to feel guilty, for had she not decided that
it was Simon's type that she preferred? She looked
down at the diamond on her left hand, and tried to
bring an image of Simon into her mind. She was
distressed that it required some effort.

Green eyes grew thoughtful as she stared through
the big picture window at the view below her. It
was growing dark now. The trees of the surrounding
forests had become a dark mass of shapes. Already

lights shone in the houses on the mountain slope, with the greatest concentration of lights near the sea, where the different villages merged one into another. She had seen so many of them today, and had marvelled at their beauty. Hout Bay, Llandudno and Clifton, hugging the shore along the Atlantic Ocean. And in False Bay, on the Indian Ocean coast of the Peninsula, there were Fish Hoek and Kalk Bay and Muizenberg. Beyond the houses was the sea. It was too dark now to see the line where water separated from sky, but Jana could make out a few lights which must belong to ships, and once she heard the distant boom of a foghorn.

She had been in the Cape a little less than a day, and already its peculiar beauty had gripped her, making her wonder how her family had summoned the strength to leave it. But that was all past history, and not something she could dwell on now. What concerned her was her reason for coming here. Before she could return to Johannesburg she must find what she needed at Devil's View. And that, she suspected already, would be more difficult than she had imagined.

Perhaps because it was mid-week and off-season, the inn was almost empty. The elderly innkeeper was not averse to sharing a sundowner with Jana. She was able to lead the conversation to Devil's View, and at mention of the wine estate his eyes lit up. 'One of the best places in the Cape,' he said.

'I want to visit it,' Jana told him.

'You know Mr Dubois?' the innkeeper asked a little curiously.

Jana felt a slight flicker of apprehension at his expression. 'Not yet,' she said cautiously.

'Not yet.... Does Mr Dubois know that you're coming?' Now the curiosity was more open.

'Well, no....'

'I see....' The words trailed away as the man rubbed a calloused hand over a balding head.

'I want to look at the house.' Jana's apprehension grew stronger, and she knew that the suspicions she had had earlier in the day had been well founded. 'Do you think I'll have any trouble?'

'Just a look?' asked the innkeeper. 'May I ask why?'

'It ...it's rather personal, I'm afraid.'

'And you say you don't know Mr Dubois?' He grimaced. 'Well, yes, I think you'll have a spot of trouble. Devil's View is not the kind of place you can just go walking into.' He frowned and added, 'Not any more.'

She seized on the words. 'Not any more?'

'Since Mr Dubois bought it over. Clint Dubois doesn't take kindly to strangers dropping in unannounced. Of course, that's not to say there aren't some who are not welcome.'

The last words were said with meaning, but Jana was not prompted to ask what he meant. Mr Clint Dubois's preference in visitors did not interest her. What concerned her was that the possibility of getting into the house and looking through the rooms, preferably the bedrooms, was becoming ever more remote.

'There's a certain Miss Maddison,' the innkeeper was saying, and his tone was disapproving. 'A model. Miss Maddison is *very* welcome at Devil's View.'

'Mr Dubois isn't married, then?' Jana was not interested in his marital status other than that it was helpful to know as much as possible about the owner of Devil's View.

'Not yet. But there's many who say it's only a matter of time now.'

Perhaps marriage would make Mr Dubois more human, but she could not wait for that to happen. She needed to get into Devil's View very soon, to-morrow if possible.

For a few minutes there was silence. The inn-keeper sipped his Martini and Jana stared thought-fully across the distant sea. At length she asked, 'Do you really think Mr Dubois would turn me away if I asked to see the house?'

'I'm afraid he might.' The man would have a heart of stone if he could refuse a little time in his house to this girl with the tiny oval face and the lovely smile, and the eyes that were as green as the trees with the sun shining through them. 'But perhaps if you told him it was just for a few minutes....'

'It wouldn't be a matter of minutes.' Jana caught her lip between small white teeth and the green eyes clouded. She didn't even know exactly where she would start her search. By the look of the house it had many rooms. 'It could be hours, even days...'

'Days?'

His curiosity had deepened. Jana toyed with an idea. Essentially honest, it was against her nature to tell lies, but the circumstances seemed to demand it. 'I'm doing research for a book on famous Cape Dutch homesteads.'

'Ah.' The innkeeper's face cleared, and she saw that her words had gone down well. 'When you said personal, I .... But a book.... There are other homesteads, Miss Harvey.'

'And I want to see them.' More improvising. 'But Devil's View has certain distinct features. I need it as a starting point.' She didn't know that her face was eloquent with pleading. 'Mr Kruger, won't you tell me a bit about Mr Dubois?'

'Let me see....' The weatherbeaten face wrinkled thoughtfully. 'He's a very rich man, and Devil's View is one of the finest estates in the Cape, but then you know that.... What more can I tell you? Clint Dubois is about thirty-five. Strong. Powerful. In command of himself.'

Involuntarily there slipped into Jana's mind the face and body of another man who fitted that description, but she pushed it determinedly away. The afternoon on the beach had no bearing on the task which lay ahead.

'Anything else?' she questioned.

'He's impatient, very impatient I should say.'

'He certainly sounds difficult,' Jana ventured.

'I should say so.' A shrug of the shoulders. 'Must be a reason why all his secretaries walk out on him.'

Jana's eyes had been on the scattered lights out at sea. Now she turned. 'Mr Dubois keeps a secretary?'

'A big estate like that entails a lot of paper-work.'

'And you say they're always leaving him?'

'All the time,' was the cheerful reply. 'Matter of fact, I heard that the last girl left him just about a week ago.'


Later that evening Jana made a phone call to Johannesburg.

'Jana? Sweetheart, is that you?'

'Oh, Simon, yes,' At the sound of his voice she relaxed. Until that moment she had not realised quite how tense she had been.

'Had a good flight?' He was talking more loudly than usual, as if he felt it was the only way to bridge the thousand-mile gap that lay between them.

'Perfect.'

'Then is there something wrong, honey?'

She heard the anxiety in his tone and smiled. How like Simon to be concerned! All at once she felt better than she had done all day. A while back, when she had been so aware of her rescuer to the extent that he had taken precedence in her mind over Simon, she had been worried. But of course she had been foolish. Simon was the only person who mattered in her life.

'Jana? Jana, you're still there?'

In her relief she had forgotten to answer him. 'Oh, yes, darling,' She laughed softly. 'I was just thinking how much I love you.'

'You're sure there's nothing wrong?' Didn't he know that the correct response was, 'I love you too'? But perhaps he would consider the statement superfluous, for it was something she was supposed to know, and superfluity in a long-distance call was unwarranted. 'You're staying at the hotel in Adderley Street?'

'No, darling. I found this inn. It's high on the mountain, and surrounded by trees and....'

'But, Jana, I told you to stay at the other place,' Annoyance had crept into his tone.

'Simon, if you could see the view from here you'd understand. I was thinking we could spend our honeymoon here, and....'

'Jana!' Now the impatience was more marked. 'This call is costing a fortune. We can talk about the honeymoon when you get back. Have you found what you're looking for?'

'No.'

'You've been to Devil's View?'

'Well, yes, in a manner of speaking.' She hesitated. 'But I haven't been inside the house.'

'Why not?'

'It's hard to explain. If you could see it you'd understand. It's not the kind of place you can just walk into....'

'Sweetheart, you're being fanciful.' A stranger might not have heard the indulgence in his tone, but Jana did not need to see her fiancé to know that he was frowning. 'Have you tried knocking on the door?'

He *was* being indulgent. Normally she would not have minded. Knowing that Simon would take care of her gave her a warm feeling, a feeling of being safe. Why on earth should it cross her mind now that he sounded as if he was speaking to a child?

'No, Simon, I haven't,' she said, and hoped that he did not notice the resentment in her tone.

'Well then. . . .'

'I told you, you'd have to see it. And besides, I gather the owner is a bit of a tyrant. Not the kind to let strange females go wandering through the bedrooms.'

'Have you met him?'

'Not yet.'

'Then I suggest you do. Tomorrow.'

'I'll try.' Jana bit her lip, uncertain how to ask the question. 'Simon, is it really necessary?'

'I think so.'

'But, darling, is it so important? Would knowing . . . I mean, would a piece of paper make any difference to the way we feel about each other?'

There was a moment of silence. When Simon answered his tone was stiff, and Jana knew that he was uneasy. 'Of course it wouldn't.'

At his words relief surged through her. 'Well then, why don't I just abandon the whole idea and catch the next plane back?'

'If we had only ourselves to consider, I'd say yes.'

The uneasiness in her fiancé's voice was more pronounced. 'But there's Mother. You know her feelings.'

'I do know.' Jana's tone was flat. It was nothing new to discover that her future mother-in-law was a snob. What *was* new, or perhaps she had never been conscious of it before, was a slight feeling of contempt that Simon would not stand up to his mother. She tried to push the thought from her mind. If Simon gave in to his mother over this issue it was purely because it was not in his nature not to hurt people—and that was one of the reasons why Jana loved him.

'You'll give it a try tomorrow?' Simon's voice came to her from a thousand miles away.

'Yes.' How foolish that she felt tension rising inside her again. 'Are you missing me?'

'Why would I be hurrying you, Jana?'

'Yes, I know. But.... Darling, you really do love me?'

'Of course I do.'

He could hardly have said otherwise, the thought flashed through her mind as she put down the phone. And then she was angry with herself. He had said it because he meant it. If he didn't love her he would not have asked her to marry him.

She went to bed earlier than usual, but though she was tired she did not fall asleep immediately. The wind had grown stronger, and as she lay in the darkness she listened to the creaking and moaning of the pine trees. The sound was soothing. Gradually she felt the tension creeping from her. She had left the curtains open, and as she stared out at the star-studded sky her mind relived the happenings of the day.

There had been her first sight of Devil's View, and the wonderment that the beautiful wine estate had once been her home. Lying in the darkness she tried to think back twenty years to a time when a little girl had run and played on the lawns in front of the big gabled house. But recollection was no clearer now than it had been earlier in the day. She thought of her drive along the mountain road and, inevitably, of her adventure in the waters of Fish Hoek.

She forced her mind on, to the talk with the innkeeper and then to the call with Simon. She was only dimly aware of the determination required to keep the image of her fiancé before her eyes. After a while even determination was not enough. As she hovered on the edge of sleep Simon slipped from her mind. The image which took his place had a mocking smile and eyes which gleamed wickedly in a gauntly handsome face.

The sun was just rising when Jana awoke the next morning. The inn was quiet, and she guessed that she had at least an hour to wait until breakfast. Pulling on a pair of jeans and a warm sweater, she slipped out of the house and into the garden. Dew hung in gossamer droplets from the branches of the pine-trees and glistened on the waxy leaves of the aloes. The sea was a translucent grey, and over the mountain the mist hung so low that she could not see more than a hundred yards up the slope. Hugging her sweater more tightly about her, she took deep breaths of the spicy forest air. She saw a trail that wound upwards through the trees and began to walk, heedless of the wet grass that clung to her sneakers.

How disapproving Mrs Lesands would be if she could see her now! Simon's mother expected her future daughter-in-law to be the epitome of well-groomed elegance at all times. And what of Simon? Jana had a suspicion that he would not be happy either if he could see her walking through the trees like a grubby woodland nymph. Not that she had any right to blame him. Simon had his career to think of. For an up-and-coming executive it could be a liability if his wife was not poised and immaculate and someone to be proud of. Which was the reason for her mission.

Her steps slowed as she thought of the task which awaited her at Devil's View. Last night, when she had reviewed the happenings of the day, she had allowed herself to forget the search. She had been too tired to think more about it, and hoped that after a night's rest things would seem clearer.

And in a sense the matter had become more clear. At least she now had a better perspective of what was involved. Any hope that Simon would tell her to abandon the search and catch the next plane home had been dashed in her telephone call. It was

also clear that she must find a way of making her
request seem so reasonable that the formidable Mr
Dubois would allow her into the house. But how?
That was the question. How was she to get around
Mr Clint Dubois?

Further she walked, and further. The haze was
gradually vanishing from the sea so that she could
make out the crested tops of the breakers and the
blurred lines of a ship. The mist on the mountain
was also beginning to lift. She wondered if, during
her brief stay at the Cape, she would have a view
of Table Mountain without its distinctive white
covering of cloud. She knew that it was the mist,
which covered the flat top of the summit like a
white cloth, which helped give the mountain its
name.

A sudden movement caught her eye and she
stood quite still. From the undergrowth scampered
a squirrel. It paused, stared at Jana, tiny eyes alert
and pointed ears quivering, then it bounded away
through the trees. Jana was smiling as she reluc-
tantly turned and made her way back to the inn.
Once again she wondered that her family had had
the heart to leave a place that was so filled with
enchantment.

A spiral of smoke rose from the chimney of the
inn, and through the air wafted a tantalising aroma
which made her walk faster. One more thing had
become clear in her mind on her way back through
the forest. It was no more than an idea at this stage,
but one which bore investigation.

At breakfast she broached her idea to the inn-keeper. At her question he looked startled, then he frowned.

'It's true, I did say a girl left Devil's View. . . .'

'Has she been replaced?' Green eyes were intent as Jana waited for his answer.

'I don't know.'

'You'd surely have heard, Mr Kruger. Devil's View is not far away.'

He was looking at her dubiously. 'You wouldn't be thinking of going to work for Mr Dubois?'

'That's exactly what I was thinking.' She couldn't help smiling at his concern. 'Don't you see, Mr Kruger? Clint Dubois needs a secretary, and I want to get an entry into Devil's View. The arrangement would suit us both.'

'You'll look after yourself?' The eyes that studied her were troubled.

Jana was touched. 'Of course I will!'

'It's said Mr Dubois can be a hard taskmaster.'

'I'll give him no cause for hardness,' Jana said gently. 'Now don't worry about me, Mr Kruger. I'll be fine.'

After breakfast she changed out of the sweater and jeans—damp and a little muddy still from her walk—into clothes more in keeping with the image of an efficient secretary: navy skirt with a red belt spanning a tiny waist. A scarlet shirt, crisp and tailored, yet fitting just snugly enough to reveal the slim curves of an intensely feminine figure. Lucky that she had brought these clothes in her suitcase. If she had to stay for any length of time she would, of course, have to buy a bigger wardrobe. With luck that would not be necessary.

She frowned into the mirror, wondering about make-up. Finally she applied a smidgin of green eye-shadow and touched long lashes with dark brown mascara. The afternoon on the beach had been sufficient to give her face a soft honey glow, and the eyes staring out of it were even bigger than usual, luminous and very green beneath a thick curtain of lashes. Despite an unusual lack of feminine vanity, Jana could not help being pleased that she was looking her best. Hard taskmaster Clint Dubois might be, but he was also a man, and as such it could only be an asset if the girl who had determined to be his future secretary was presentable.

At the last minute she took off her ring and put it in her purse. Mr Dubois might be more amenable to a prospective secretary who appeared to have no encumbrances. That she was thereby not being quite honest did not occur to her.

Jana's feelings as she approached the tall iron gates of Devil's View were not quite the same as those of the previous day. It was impossible to be unaware of the beauty of the gracious Cape Dutch homestead, but this time her appreciation was on a more abstract level. As she got out of the car to open the gates so that she could proceed up the long oak-lined drive, her thoughts were solely on the forthcoming meeting with Clint Dubois. If he was as hard a man as the innkeeper had described him, she would need all her wits to achieve what she wanted.

There had been a moment when she had thought of phoning the owner of Devil's View to make an appointment, but she had decided against it. It would have been too easy for Mr Dubois to say he would not see her. Much better to confront him face to face, without warning. That way, even if he started by refusing her, she could try on him her full powers of persuasion. She would not, she resolved, give up her quest without a fight.

As she stopped the car on the sweep of drive to one side of the house she thought once more of Simon. It required a degree of firmness to push away the little voice that said that if he loved her enough he would not be putting her through this ordeal.

Mounting stone steps leading to the great carved door with the gleaming brass knocker, she tried to visualise herself clambering over these same steps as a small child. There was a vague memory of black stone, of a doll, a woman's laughing voice. But that was all. The memories were too vague to be meaningful.

A house-servant in immaculate uniform opened the door. There was an impassive reaction when she asked for Mr Dubois, and then she was led into a room that was presumably the library. Jana looked about her as she waited, and despite her nervousness she could not help being fascinated. She thought she had never seen a more beautiful room. It seemed to radiate a sense of light and spaciousness. The furniture was all stinkwood and leather. There was a desk, with a lovely hand-carved inlay, and bookcases with books which had a look of having been read many times. There were leather chairs, big and with an air of extreme comfort. And pictures, mainly by South African artists. Jana walked over to a painting which could only be by Pierneef, the man who had immortalised so much of the countryside, and whose work she had seen only in art galleries. As she studied the landscape of mountains and bluegums, she thought that the artist must have loved his homeland very much to be able to paint it so well.

Sun flooded through the tall windows, and where it caught the dark wood the patina glowed with life. Every object in the room indicated expense, and yet superseding the luxury was a sense of comfort and rightness. As Jana gazed about her, Clint Dubois went up in her esteem. Hard taskmaster he might very well be. He was also a man of culture and unique good taste.

'Miss Harvey?'

Just two words, clipped and a little impatient. But the voice was familiar. Jana spun around.

'I didn't hear you come in. . . .' The words trailed away, as she felt the blood drain from her limbs. She put a hand to the back of a chair.

The gesture was not lost on him. Even through

her shock she saw the derisive curl of the lips, the gleam of amusement in the dark eyes. 'Then it's not just in the sea that you lose control over your limbs?' he asked conversationally.

# CHAPTER THREE

So he *had* recognised her. For a wild moment she had hoped that he would not associate her with the girl he had rescued in the waves.

'I'm in perfect control of myself,' she assured him icily, taking her hand from the chair as if to prove her point. Glancing at a point behind him, she stood very straight as she braced herself for his reply. Instinctively she knew it would be sarcastic.

But he did not speak. After a moment she allowed her gaze to return to him, and instantly she was sorry. For in the eyes that held hers was a quality that was infinitely more devastating than any verbal response he could have made. Insolently his eyes rested on her face, flushed now that the blood had returned to it. Then slowly, deliberately, his gaze travelled downwards, from the slender throat with the pulse throbbing at its base to the feminine curves of the slender body. It needed no words to tell Jana that he was reconstructing yesterday's incident, and that he was remembering the way she had lain against him in the water. She was remembering it too. But did he need to be quite so blatant about it?

It was only by sheer effort of will that she managed to speak with a modicum of calm. 'I came to see Mr Dubois.'

The grey eyes left her body, coming up to rest on her face once more. The amusement had deepened. 'I am Clint Dubois.'

Though she had expected it, nevertheless the statement came as a shock. 'You ... you....' she began to stammer, and then, recovering herself, she injected a note of accusation into her tone. 'You let me think you were a lifeguard!'

'You drew your own conclusions,' he reminded her mildly.

'You rescued me....' It was a foolish thing to say, but Jana's senses were reacting so dramatically to this tall lean man that she was finding it difficult to think.

'Would you have preferred it if I'd let you drown?' Again the sparkle in the dark eyes. 'That wasn't why you swam out of your depth in the first place, I presume?'

'I was not out of my depth,' she said crossly. 'I just happened to get caught in a whirlpool.' And then, as a well-shaped brow lifted in apparent disbelief: 'I should have known you would go on believing what you want to believe.'

'Perhaps you'd like to tell me the purpose of your visit, Miss Harvey?' The blandness in his tone, and the adroitness with which he had changed the subject, indicated that he did not in fact believe her story. 'Have you come to repeat your gratitude?'

He was baiting her again. Was he always so obnoxious? Jana wondered, as she met the sardonic gaze in the rugged-featured face. Clint Dubois had all the qualities she most detested in a man—arrogance, an aura of power and wealth and authority, a hint of ruthlessness. He was good-looking, though not in a conventional sense. Perhaps it was the aura of sensualness and virile strength which she had noticed before which made him more arresting than any man she had met. Women would be drawn to him wherever he went. A certain kind of woman, she corrected herself mentally, and had a fleeting vision of the girl he had called Miranda. It was impossible that Clint Dubois was unaware of his physical magnetism—another mark against him as far as Jana was concerned.

'I have *not* come to express my gratitude,' she said, his manner provoking her to a matter-of-factness that was alien to her nature. 'I expressed it yesterday.'

There was a momentary glimmer in the dark eyes. Not amusement this time, but something else which Jana couldn't define. A little apprehensively she wondered if she had gone too far. She had come to Devil's View for a purpose, and it would be foolish to let her dislike of its owner stand in the way of what she had to do.

'Please take a seat, Miss Harvey.' He was wholly the master of the estate now, well-dressed, brisk, but without any attempt at real friendliness. 'It was remiss of me not to have suggested it earlier, but'—again the deliberate glance over her body—'the circumstances of our first meeting must have distracted me.'

'Has anyone ever told you you're insufferable?' It was out before she could stop herself. In consternation she clamped a hand over her mouth, as if the gesture could retract the words. Green eyes were wide with apprehension as she stared at him.

'You have—now.' His eyes were hard. 'I'm a busy man, Miss Harvey. Get to the point.'

She couldn't meet that implacable gaze for more than a moment. She felt sick with nervousness as her eyes skittered away from his face, a spare and chiselled mask, and with the same degree of coldness. Her mouth had gone so dry that she did not know if she could speak. With an effort she swallowed.

'I want to work for you,' she managed at last.

Once again his reaction was not what she expected. She was prepared to cope with astonishment, even a certain amount of derision. But his laughter, low and sensual, was unnerving.

She jerked around, and looked at him questioningly. 'That wasn't intended as a joke.'

'No?' Another low chuckle. 'I take it you've read all the best manuals on how to approach a job-interview?'

'If you mean....' A small pink tongue went out to moisten the dry lips. 'I started badly, I know. But I didn't expect.... I didn't know....'

'That you'd come face to face with the reprehensible man who took advantage of you in the water yesterday.' White teeth flashed wickedly in the tanned face. 'I'm sure it was a shock. Now I want to hear just what it is you want to do for me.'

She shot him a quick glance, but there was an enigmatic watchfulness in his expression which made her look away again. The interview was proving even more difficult than she had imagined. She took a deep steadying breath.

'I want to be your secretary.'

'Well,' he said, and the mocking note in his tone brought a swift flush to her cheeks, 'That's very interesting.'

Bravely she faced him. 'Why?'

'There must be a reason why you've come all the way to Devil's View for a job.'

'I . . . I believed you needed a secretary. . . .'

'And that's all there is to it?' He spoke with a quiet laziness.

'Should there be more?' She looked at him uncertainly. The laziness in his tone was reflected in the smiling curve of his lips, but Jana noticed that it did not extend to his eyes. He sat quite still, leaning back in the deep leather armchair, one long muscled leg resting casually across the other, yet for all his ease there was something about him which made Jana think of a beast of prey, strong and powerful and infinitely dangerous.

'I think so.'

She adopted what she hoped was a confident manner. 'You need a secretary. I need a job.'

'That may be so.' Somehow the air of danger increased. 'But it strikes me that there must be something more. There's no shortage of jobs in

Cape Town. And,' he paused, 'I haven't advertised the position.'

'I ... I heard that a secretary had left you not long ago....'

'That's correct,' he acknowledged.

'And that she hadn't been replaced.'

'That's correct too.'

'Well then!' A defiant shrug of the shoulders. 'Doesn't that put an end to the mystery?'

'No.' He took a pipe from the pocket of his trousers, and Jana noticed that his fingers were long and well-shaped. He took his time about lighting it, not seeming to notice the silence that lay between them like a stone wall. Jana was so tense with nerves and frustration that she could have screamed.

At length he looked up. 'You're not stupid, Miss Harvey. Neither am I. We both know that we're just sparring. You have a definite reason for wanting to be at Devil's View, and I want to know what it is.'

Simon, Jana thought, is this ordeal really necessary? Aloud she said, 'You're right, Mr Dubois. I do have a reason.'

'Ah!' The watchfulness deepened.

Emerald eyes were concealed beneath lids fringed with long sooty lashes as Jana wondered how she should put her case to him. Her impulse was to tell him the truth. She had the impression that Clint Dubois was a man who would value integrity. There was nothing wrong with her mission, and had Mr Dubois been a different sort of person there would be no need for subterfuge. But the owner of Devil's View was unlike anyone she had ever met, and she knew with curious certainty that he would think her quest quite absurd.

Which left only the story she had told the innkeeper.

'So you're interested in Cape Dutch architecture.' The statement was casual enough, and Jana hoped the calculated gleam in his eyes was purely a figment of her over-sensitive imagination.

'Yes,' she smiled.

'Now why is it that I don't believe you?' At her gasp there was a satisfied chuckle. 'I thought that would wipe the sugary smile from your face.'

'Mr Dubois. . . .' Forgetful of her quest, forgetful of anything but the sheer arrogance of the man, she jumped to her feet. 'If you don't want me, say so. I certainly don't need. . .'

'Ah, but you do.' A hand shot out, imprisoning her wrist in a grip of iron and forcing her back into her seat. 'You do need the job. Though for what reason I don't know.' He grinned, a grin that was wicked and satisfied. 'And it just so happens that I need a secretary.'

She looked at him uncertainly. His hand had left her wrist, but where he had touched her the skin was tingling as if it had been in contact with an electric current. Somehow he had managed to get the upper hand, and though, basically, it suited her purpose, she was consumed with a desire to defy him.

'You're saying you don't believe me,' she returned at last.

'Not a word of it,' he agreed cheerfully.

'Then I can't see why you should want to hire me,' she said flatly.

'Quite simple. I can use you—providing you can spell and have the rudiments of a few other basic skills. You *can* spell, I take it?'

'Like to test me?'

The question was loaded with defiance. As she waited for his answer her eyes were blazing pools of green. Part of her knew she was provoking him to reject her. The result would be a confrontation with Simon and his mother. It would be a confrontation which, in her defiant state of mind, seemed not inappropriate. The other part acknowledged that she wanted this job. Vaguely she understood that the desire to work at Devil's View had as much to do with its arrogant and disturbing owner as with the fact that she had a mission to accomplish. There was something infinitely disturbing in that thought, but Jana's state of mind was momentarily so chaotic that it would need time and privacy for her to sort out her thoughts.

'A test is unnecessary.' His glance was a taunt. 'If you don't come up to scratch I won't be shy to send you packing.'

'I'd be just one more in the line,' she responded recklessly, and caught her breath at the harshness in the dark eyes.

'So you've been listening to stories.'

She cursed the colour which swept her cheeks. Damn the man! Was it his compelling maleness which endowed the most harmless remark with more meaning than it deserved? She saw the glint in his eyes, and knew that he had registered her embarrassment. Even now, when the job was more or less hers, she wondered if she should abandon the whole thing.

'I couldn't help hearing some talk,' she tossed back at him.

'Which makes it all the more strange that you should want to expose yourself to the same treatment.' There was a look of searching in the rugged features. 'Well, Miss Harvey?'

She managed a smile. 'If you want me, I'll be happy to work for you.'

At his look of approval there was a moment of absurd happiness. But there was no time to examine the feeling, for he was talking once more.

'There is one condition, Miss Harvey.'

'A condition?'

'You'll have to live here at Devil's View.'

He had spoken in a tone of extreme mildness, but his words knocked the breath from her lungs so that for a moment she could not speak. He was watching her, one eyebrow lifted slightly, the corners of his mouth curving in a very slight smile.

'That's impossible,' she managed at length.

'Then there's no job,' he informed her crisply.

'So that's why your secretaries leave you, one after the other,' she accused.

His laughter was derisive. 'If you think that, then you don't know your sex very well, Miss Harvey.'

It came to her, as she studied the implacable eyes and the lips that were hard and sensuous at the same time, that Clint Dubois had a very low opinion of women. And she wondered why that should matter to her.

As for his condition—she needed the job. Clearly there was no sense in unnecessary sparring with an adversary who would win every time, but the stipulation was so outrageous that it needed clarification.

'Why do I need to sl—to stay here overnight?' she asked haltingly.

'Because I don't always have a regular dictating routine. The matters of the estate come first every time, Miss Harvey. That's something you must understand if you work for me.' He paused. 'I won't make many demands on you, but if I want something done in the evenings I need you to be here.'

'It's an intolerable situation,' she burst out.

'The choice is yours.' His voice was flat.

She looked away from him as she turned the proposition around in her mind. In one sense it was as intolerable as she had said. There might be gossip, of course, but strangely that was the aspect that worried her least. She knew few people in Cape Town. In any event, it was unlikely that she would be at Devil's View long enough for gossip to take a hold.

What disturbed her far more than any potential

scandalmongering was the thought of being alone at night with Clint Dubois. There was something too compellingly and aggressively male about him for the idea to be a comfortable one.

Nevertheless, the situation did have an advantage, and Jana was quick to see it. Living at Devil's View she would have the run of the house more or less. There would be many times when its owner would be out in the lands or away for the evening, and she would be able to go on with her search undisturbed.

When she turned back to him she knew that he had been watching her. Impossible as it was, she had the odd feeling that he knew the gist of her thoughts.

The small pointed chin lifted. 'I accept the position, Mr Dubois.'

'Then there's just the salary to be discussed,' he said, and from his tone she knew that he had taken her acceptance for granted.

She had risen from her chair and was on her way to the door when she turned slightly. 'My door will be kept locked at night.'

The laughter was sensual and amused and so close to her that she felt a quiver run through her nerve-stream. She had not realised that he had followed her to the door. When he spoke his breath fanned a hot cheek.

'If I wanted you, do you think a locked door would keep me out?'

'You wouldn't dare,' she whispered through a parched throat.

'You don't think so?'

He took another step towards her. He did not put his arms around her as she expected, but stood quite still. She could feel the tautness of the hard thighs, just barely touching her, and was achingly aware of the broad chest. Yesterday's closeness was a memory that flooded through her senses. In a way, what was happening now was even more tantalising. Her nostrils were filled with the smell of maleness, and her heart was pounding so wildly that she wondered if he could hear it.

'Well, Miss Harvey?' A soft sensuous taunt.

'I....' It was increasingly hard to swallow. 'I'd hope ... that you'd be ... a gentleman.'

His laughter sent the blood shivering through her veins. 'Gentlemen in an age where there are no more ladies? Perhaps you've changed your mind, Miss Harvey?'

Numbly she shook her head.

She heard his swift intake of breath. Then he stepped away from her with an abruptness which, while it relieved her, also left her feeling strangely bereft.

'I'll expect you tomorrow at nine,' he said, and when she looked up at him she saw that his eyes were bleak.

Even now it was not too late to change her mind,

Jana reasoned, as she took the road that led to the inn. When they had discussed salary—the size of which had astonished her—Clint had also made clear in what way notice could be given. He had bound himself to a month, but had agreed that on Jana's part a week would be sufficient.

What would he say if she decided to turn down the job now, before it had even begun? He might be angry, but she doubted that he would be surprised. Clint Dubois seemed to have a contemptuous view of women which would prevent him from being shocked by anything they might do.

When she got to the inn she would phone Simon. She could reach him at his office. What would be his reaction when he learned that she had taken a job which would keep her in Cape Town for some time? And what of the fact that her nights would be spent at Devil's View? What would he say to that? She took her eyes momentarily from the road and glanced down at her bare finger. Simon seemed so very far away. It was a distance which was more than a mere geographical one of a thousand miles. For some reason, one which she did not care to analyse too deeply, the fact of her engagement seemed to have become like something in a dream, ephemeral and insubstantial, as if it had existed at some other time, in some other world. The thought was disturbing.

At a place where the road had been widened to allow for a viewpoint, she drew the car to an abrupt halt. Taking the ring from her purse, she pushed it firmly and deliberately on to her finger. Then she opened the door and walked to the edge of the sandy verge.

Below her lay a vista of vineyards, a lovely blending of green and purple. The wind was gentle, a south-easter which carried the salty tang of the sea. The mist had cleared, and above her the shape of the mountain was a sharp straight line against the sky.

Green eyes clouded with thought as she stood at the lonely viewpoint and looked toward the horizon. There had to be a reason for the way she felt. She loved Simon; she wanted to be married to him. The engagement was the only reason for her being here, for her mission at Devil's View. Whatever her own thoughts on the matter, the search was of importance to Simon and his mother, and in consequence must be of importance to Jana herself.

Her engagement was the one solid fact in all the present circumstances, and therefore the feeling of dreamlike insubstantiality made no sense at all. She glanced down at her ring. The sun caught at the diamond, firing it with a brilliant kaleidoscope of colour. The diamond in itself meant nothing to Jana. Its sole importance lay in what it represented—Simon, and their future life together.

But she would have to be careful. The mere fact that she was having to sort things out in her mind was proof of that. The beauty of the Peninsula, the unexpected loveliness of Devil's View, and the compelling aura of its owner, combined to make a potent magic which could dazzle the senses of the most sensible girl. The important thing was that she was aware of the magic and could therefore take precautions to avoid becoming affected by it.

When she had found what she needed, Clint Dubois and his home would become a memory. An exciting memory perhaps, but one that would fade as she became more and more occupied with the business of being Mrs Simon Lesands, of running a home and looking after a husband.

She turned her head at the sound of a car. It was long and streamlined, like a swift silver fish. It slowed very slightly as it passed the spot where Jana stood, but did not stop. If the driver had seen her, he did nothing to acknowledge it. She did not see his face, but the confident tilt of the dark head was becoming rapidly familiar. As she watched the car disappear down the road, negotiating the steep bends with a swift and deceptive ease, she was aware that her breath had quickened.

The beauty seemed to have vanished from the scene below her, and with an anger that was irrational she walked back to the Mini. Logic and caution were all very well, she told herself with an unwilling flash of insight. Even more important was the need to accomplish her mission with the utmost speed, so that she could put Devil's View and its owner out of her mind as quickly as possible.

'You've found it, sweetheart?' Simon's voice was eager.

'Not yet.'

She wondered why it should irritate her that he should think it necessary to speak so loudly simply because it was a long-distance call, or why she should be annoyed that he went straight to the point. With the seconds ticking away at an exorbitant cost it was surely self-evident that trivialities must be dispensed with. If one thought of them as trivialities. . . .

'What's holding you up?'

'I told you it wouldn't be easy. . . .' Her voice begged for understanding.

'You've looked, though?'

'No. . . .'

She broke off and saw that the knuckles of the hand holding the receiver were white and clammy. Deliberately she relaxed the unnecessary grip.

'Jana!' It was a disagreeable bark.

'Simon . . . sweetheart. . . .' Why was she pleading with him? It was Simon's idea that she go on this trip. 'I haven't had a chance yet. It's . . . well. . . .' Again the words tapered off.

'For heaven's sake, Jana! Take a hold of yourself. These calls are costing a fortune. Surely you can try to be concise.'

Hardly lover-like. Biting her lip to choke back an instinctive retort, she looked at her ring. The cold stone winked back at her, reminding her that the man at the other end of the line loved her and wanted her to be his wife.

She took a deep breath. 'I've taken a job as secretary at Devil's View.'

'You don't mean that!'

She continued as if he hadn't spoken, her tone level. 'I start tomorrow.'

'Is this necessary?'

'It's the only way I can get into the house.'

'Well, in that case, it seems there's no alternative.'

Stupid to be annoyed by his easy compliance. 'There's something you should know,' she told him, and her voice was grim.

'Yes?'

'I'll be sleeping at Devil's View.'

She held her breath.

'The hell you're not!' The exclamation was angry, indignant. Jana expelled her breath and relaxed. Things would be all right after all. She had been wrong even to doubt Simon.

'It's a condition of employment,' she told him.

There was a long silence. For once Simon seemed unaware of the expensive passing of time. When he spoke it was with resignation. 'If that's the condition, then it seems you have no choice.'

'You—don't mind?' she asked, when she had found her voice.

'Of course I mind.' The response was swift. 'No man worth his salt fancies the idea of his fiancée spending her nights in another man's home.'

'Well then?' she demanded.

'Honey,' he said, and though his tone was indulgent and reasonable she could hear the iritation behind it, 'you present me with a fait accompli. What's more, you tell me it's a condition of the employment. What do you expect me to say?'

'I thought you might tell me to drop the whole idea,' she said dully.

'Sweetheart, it's what I'd like....'

'Well, then?' she asked again.

'You know the importance of what you're looking for.' His tone held a finality that was chilling.

'Yes,' she said, and wondered if he heard the bleakness in her tone. 'It might take some time, Simon.'

'I understand.'

She was incensed by his reasonableness. 'This call is costing a fortune,' she reminded him icily.

'We'll say goodbye. Jana, sweetheart,'—there was warmth in his voice now, and pleading, as if he realised that he had angered her—'I'll be thinking of you every moment. I love you, sweetheart.'

'I love you too,' she said, and was horrified by the mechanical ring of the statement.

As she put down the receiver her anger was replaced by a chilling numbness. The thought that came to mind was involuntary. She could not help wondering if Clint Dubois, in similar circumstances, would allow the woman he loved to go on with her mission.

## CHAPTER FOUR

SHE arrived at Devil's View five minutes before the hour. The servant who had opened the door for her the day before smiled in recognition and asked her to follow him. Her employer was in his office, a large sunny room not far from the library. He was writing, the dark head bent so that Jana could not see his eyes.

'Mr Dubois,' she said tentatively.

'I'm glad you're punctual.' His voice was crisp and matter-of-fact, making nonsense of her nervousness. Jana told herself that she was glad he was putting their relationship on an impersonal footing.

He put down his pen and stood up, and unaccountably her pulses quickened. She had forgotten quite how tall he was. His shoulders were broader than she remembered them, and through the clinging fabric of a cotton-knit shirt she could see the muscled contours of his chest.

He took a step towards her. The eyes that studied her, taking in every detail of her appearance, were dark and very steady. As if mesmerised, she could only stare back at him.

Quite suddenly he smiled, and with it warmth lit his eyes. It came to Jana that Clint Dubois could be human when he chose. 'Welcome to Devil's View,' he said.

'Thank you,' she said softly, and as she felt the nervousness leave her, she smiled back at him.

A moment later it was back, and tension with it, gripping the muscles of her stomach in a hard painful knot. For her smile seemed to have wrought some change in him. The warmth had vanished from his face. Grey eyes stared down at her, hard and implacable.

'I'll have the housekeeper show you to your room.' A long tanned hand reached for a bell and pressed it. 'Can you be ready to begin work in half an hour?'

'Of course,' she said lightly, matching his matter-of-factness.

But as she followed the housekeeper through the long passages of the house, she was aware of a feeling of bleakness. It was all very well to tell herself that Clint Dubois was nothing more than her employer. The knowledge that he held her in contempt—for there was no other way in which she could explain his behaviour—was hurtful.

The house was even bigger than she had realised. As they came into what must be the bedroom wing Jana looked about her with interest, and then a growing despair. So many doors ... and no way of knowing in which of these rooms was the thing she was looking for. Would her stay at Devil's View be even longer than she had anticipated?

The housekeeper opened a door, then stepped aside and waited for her to enter. The feeling of depression lifted as Jana looked about her entranced. Like the other rooms she had seen so far, this had a feeling of light and air and sunshine on polished wood. The curtains and the bedspread were a dusty pink brocade, and the carpet was a soft pearl grey. The furniture was all stinkwood; a graceful dresser, a bookcase, a small round table beside the bed.

When the housekeeper had left her, Jana went to the big bay window with its curved cushioned seat. She could not see the ocean, but there was a view of gardens and vineyards. She stood looking out a few moments, then turned and studied the room once more. Who had slept here more than twenty years ago? She searched her mind for a memory, but none came.

Her eyes grew thoughtful as she looked about her. In the first moment of enchantment she had seen only the brightness of the room, the tasteful furnishings and the lovely blending of colour. She had not noticed the panelling on the walls. There had been panelling in the library, and in the office. Was it naïve to hope that the other rooms in the house were not panelled as well?

She glanced at her watch. If she wanted to unpack she must move quickly. Half an hour, he had told her, and she had no doubt that he was a man who meant what he said.

Of their own volition her thoughts turned to Clint Dubois. If he was physically the most arresting man she she met, he was also the most unnerving. She had no doubt that he could be charming when he chose. But neither did she have any illusions about his arrogance, his ruthlessness. Would she be able to endure living in the same house as this man, working for him, putting up with his unpredictable moods? The whole set-up was intolerable. She was tempted to go back to his office and tell him what he could do with his job—just as all his other secretaries had evidently done. And yet she could not do it. She had come to Devil's View with a purpose, and because she loved Simon she must go through with it.

When she returned to him he showed her the room where she would work. It was a smaller room, adjoining the main office, efficiently furnished with a desk, an electric typewriter and steel filing cabinets. The modern office equipment contrasted starkly with the lovely antiques and gracious furniture Jana had glimpsed thus far.

He began to explain her duties. His tone was cool, his expression, when he deigned to look at her, calm and utterly remote. Allowing him to set the tone, Jana responded with as detached and efficient a manner as she could muster. Now and then, when his head was bent, she was able to study him unobserved. It was hard to believe that Clint Dubois, the cool and efficient master of the estate, was the man she had first met in the waves. That man had been a sea-god, wild and primitive and earthy. She could only marvel at the change in him. And yet, despite the differences in his outer appearance and manner, she was as aware of him now

as she had been that first time. The trappings of
expensive clothes and a slightly more civilised manner could not hide the essential aura of the
man, the sense of maleness and sensual virility
which Jana had never encountered before. Wryly
she wondered whether Simon would have been
quite so ready to agree to the conditions of her employment if he had met her employer.

The range of her duties was more extensive than
she had first anticipated. Despite the fact that her
employment could be only of relatively short dura-
tion, and was only an excuse to get an entry into
the house, Jana found herself listening with rapt
attention while Clint Dubois spoke. The work
sounded so interesting that she caught herself wishing the job was permanent. But of course that could
never be. Permanence was Simon. Permanence was
marriage, and being a good wife and hostess for
a fast-climbing executive. And of course, though
Simon was not as enthusiastic on this point as she
was, it would also mean motherhood.

When he had finished explaining her duties, Clint
began to dictate. Jana's shorthand was good, but
she soon realised that she must get accustomed to
a whole new terminology—Rieslings and rosés, vats
and vintages. At an unfamiliar word she hesitated,
uncertain of what he had said.

She looked up, wanting him to repeat himself,
and saw that he had been watching her. There was
a watchfulness in the dark grey eyes which she had
noticed before. There was also something else,

which sent a quick warmth to her cheeks.

'New territory?' he asked dryly.

'A little. But I'm sure I'll manage,' she countered swiftly.

'I've no doubt you manage most things you set your mind to.' There was a challenging quality in his expression, and Jana had the curious feeling that they were talking about something other than office procedure.

She felt impelled to answer him, but was at a loss for words. For a long moment green eyes stared into grey ones. Jana was the first to look away.

The dictation resumed, as remote and efficient as before, and Jana wondered if she had imagined the subtle meaning behind the interchange. Only when Clint Dubois rose to go was there a momentary return of the sardonic quality which was rapidly becoming familiar.

'Don't hesitate to ask for help if you get stuck, Miss Harvey.' He paused, and she saw the glimmer of amusement. 'Don't wait until you're way beyond your depth.'

Jana had been at Devil's View three days before she was able to start her search. The first two days had been so busy that she had not been able to think of it. Clint Dubois was a demanding employer. He was not unfair, but he set a high standard and expected it to be met. In return he paid a good salary. Jana was beginning to understand why he had had a turn-over of secretaries. From the little she had seen of her predecessors' work, it seemed that the girls who were drawn to the job because of its glamour were disillusioned when they realised what it entailed.

One of Mr Dubois's maxims was that today's work must be done today. Jana was determined that she would show him that she could keep up with his pace. More was involved than the desire to stay at Devil's View until she was ready to go. It came to her with a slight sense of surprise that her employer's respect was important to her.

Work was not the only thing that kept her from her quest. As yet the house was a strange place. There were so many rooms, and so many people moving about. As yet she did not know the routine of the housekeeper and the two maids. The last thing she wanted was to be discovered in a compromising situation with no adequate excuse.

But on the third day there was still an hour till lunch when she had finished her work. Clint was out in the vineyards, and the house was empty. She had already observed that this was a time which the staff spent in their quarters.

Leaving the letters she had typed in a neat pile on her desk, Jana left the office and walked to the bedroom wing. Her heart was beating faster than usual. It was not as if she was about to do something criminal. What she was looking for was a thing which belonged to her; a thing which had been at Devil's View for more than twenty years; hers to retrieve if ever she wanted it.

Nevertheless she felt ill at ease. She would be in a spot if Clint were to find her. He would demand to know what she was doing. In a way she wished now that she had been honest with him from the start; it would have spared her the whole charade of being his secretary. In retrospect she wondered if she had been foolish to allow herself to be daunted by the grandeur of Devil's View, and by the forceful personality of its owner. And yet—and here she was back to her original line of thinking—would Clint Dubois have agreed to a search? Unlikely. More than ever, now that she knew him she felt that her quest would have earned his contempt. Which brought her thinking back full circle. The whole affair must remain a secret.

There were seven rooms in the bedroom wing, and so far she had seen only her own. She knew where Clint slept. His room was just three doors away from hers. She said a silent prayer that it would not be necessary to search there, that she would find what she was looking for elsewhere.

It was very quiet in the house. There was only the sound of her pounding heart, so loud that Jana was certain it could be heard at a distance. The temptation was to abandon the search, or at least to put it off to another day. But a start had to be made. Deliberately she opened the door next to hers and stepped into the room.

Her despair mounted as she went from one room to the next. It was as she had feared: everywhere was panelling. In the end there was only one room left to see. She put her hand to the door, then glanced quickly along the passage, hating the need for furtiveness.

The room was panelled too; she took in at a glance. She could have gone then, for she had wanted to know only what she was faced with. But still she looked about her, caught by the character of the room. Though it was empty it was filled with the aura of its owner; there was the same sense of strictness, of unyielding authority. She shook herself impatiently. She was allowing the straight lines, the tidiness, coupled with her heightened sense of the dramatic, to get the better of her. It was only a room and she was imagining things. But she could not shrug away the feeling that this was a masculine abode, filled with the same forceful virility as its owner.

There was the sound of a door closing somewhere in the house. Hastily Jana left Clint's room. She was thoughtful as she stood before her mirror and brushed her hair. Today she had done no more than case the joint, so to speak. She would have to search the rooms one by one, and that would take time. It was evident that her stay at Devil's View would be very much longer than she had ever anticipated.

He was seated at the great stinkwood table when she came into the dining-room, and instinctively she halted. She dreaded the meals which they ate together. Till now she had been lucky; Clint breakfasted early and was out in the vineyards before she came down. Lunch was evidently an unpredictable meal. Sometimes he ate at Devil's View, often elsewhere. So far there had been only dinner to contend with, and she had found it a strain to sit with him at the big table while the servants waited on them. The first day she had suggested that she take her meals on a tray in her room, but he had disposed of the suggestion with a decisiveness which did not allow for argument. He saw no reason, he said, to put the staff to the inconvenience of serving a meal in two different places.

He looked up as she came in, and she saw by the lift of his eyebrows that he had registered her moment of hesitation. She was about to sit where she had sat before, at the other side of the table, but he gestured to the chair beside him.

'That's not my seat,' she said foolishly.

'It is now. Come, Miss Harvey, the food will get cold.'

With as much dignity as she could muster she took the chair next to his. A plate of soup was put before her, and she forced herself to swallow a few spoonfuls. It was not easy to eat with Clint Dubois's unnerving presence so close beside her.

'Why have you changed the seating arrangements?' she asked when the maid had left the room.

'Because it pleases me.'

The words were spoken with a calm self-assurance. It came to Jana that Clint Dubois would always do exactly what pleased him, whether it concerned his estate, his wines or his women. Beneath

long thick-lashed green eyes she stole a glance at
him. He was watching her. There was just the
slightest upward tilt at the corners of his mouth,
and she had the feeling that he was laughing at her.

'There's surely no cause for an argument,' he
drawled lazily. 'Even you must see that it makes
more sense to sit like this than to conduct a shouted
conversation from opposite sides of the table.'

She was taken aback. Though the idea of social
conversation with Clint Dubois was daunting, it
was at the same time curiously tantalising.

'You mean we'll be discussing our work at meal-
times?' she asked demurely, deliberately misunder-
standing him.

'Not quite what I had in mind.' His voice was
low, with a quality that was both teasing and provocative. She saw him put down his knife. Then a
tanned lean-fingered hand reached for her chin,
forcing her to look at him. 'But I'll let you choose
the topic.'

Not a moment too soon the hand left her chin.
Her face tingled from his touch, and she knew that
her cheeks were burning. Damn the man! she
thought vehemently. He could hardly be unaware
of the response he provoked, and from the gleam in
the dark eyes it was evident that it amused him. She
dropped her eyes and kept them on her food while
she made a pretence of eating. He was too precep-
tive a man not to guess that his touch had embar-
rassed her, but there was no need for him to know
that it had also been a kind of delight.

'You're afraid of me.'

Her head jerked up. His eyes were on her face, watchful, mocking, subjecting her to a scrutiny which was becoming familiar.

'Whatever gave you that idea?' If only she did not sound quite so breathless!

'The way you're sitting there, like a prim virgin scared stiff that she's about to be raped.' The laziness in his tone made the statement all the more outrageous.

'You're quite wrong.' She tried to suppress the quiver in her own voice. 'I wasn't expecting to be raped.'

'Nor are you prim, though you like to give that impression.' A wicked chuckle. 'But you *are* a virgin.'

'You make it sound like an insult.' Her voice was a little unsteady.

'Make of it what you will.' Again the touch of mockery. 'This does happen to be the twentieth century, Miss Harvey.'

'Which doesn't mean that I've abandoned all morals,' she countered.

'The prim Miss Harvey—who wasn't all that prim in the waves the other day.' His laughter had a quality which set her pulses racing. 'Don't bother to deny it. Eat up instead. Maggie will be upset if you leave her food untouched.'

'You're the most arrogant man I've ever met!' she flung at him.

'But you still want to work for me.' His voice was very mild, very dangerous.

She drew a deep breath. '... Yes.'

'You must be very strong-minded on the subject of Cape-Dutch houses.'

'I am.'

She held her knife and fork tightly, cutting her food with grim determination. He was baiting her now, and she was bracing herself to withstand him.

His next words were unexpected. 'You finished work early this morning.'

There was nothing untoward in the statement, but she shot him an involuntary glance. She had been so certain that she was alone in the house when she began her tour of the bedroom wing. Was it possible that he had got wind of it somehow?

'I'm getting into the routine,' she said evenly.

'And I've nothing for you this afternoon.' He paused. 'Perhaps you'd like to see something of Devil's View?'

'You mean the rooms?' she asked swiftly, more certain than ever that he had seen her opening doors and was looking for a way to punish her.

'I mean the estate. The architecture that you were so interested in.' His eyes were narrow. 'That *is* why you're here, isn't it?'

'Yes ... yes, of course.'

'Then I'd imagine you'd be glad of a chance to look around.'

She darted him a deliberate smile. 'I'd like it very much. As you've nothing for me to do, I probably shall begin wandering around the estate this afternoon.'

'You'd be far better off wandering with me.'

His tone was casual, but as her eyes met his gaze she realised that the invitation was anything but casual. He had made the offer quite deliberately. Because he didn't want her roaming the grounds on her own? Or because he wanted her company? The second thought was totally absurd, and she dispensed with it immediately. Clint Dubois had made his indifference to her clear enough.

But if an afternoon spent together meant nothing to him, it came to Jana in a moment of astonishing self-revelation that it did mean something to her. Unaccountably her heart was beating more quickly, and she felt the swift warmth rising in her cheeks. His gaze still held hers, steady grey eyes looking into wide startled green ones.

'The thought of my company is so distasteful?' A dark brow lifted sardonically.

Distasteful? Oh no! Exciting. Tantalising. The words sprang to mind without volition. Aloud she said, lightly, 'Heavens, no. I was just surprised that ... well, that you'd have the time....'

'We'll go when you've had your coffee.'

'That will be nice,' she said inadequately. With fingers that shook she lifted her cup to her lips. She drank the coffee in tiny sips, trying to prolong the moment when she must leave the house with her disturbing employer. Not only her fingers were shaking; her entire nerve-stream was quivering with the shock of a realization which she could not accept. Would never accept.

When she had finished her coffee she left the dining room on the pretext that she needed pen and paper from her room so that she could make notes. In reality she wanted only to get away from him for a few minutes, so that she could calm herself and collect her thoughts. She was behaving like a very young girl on her first date. In fact, she was being completely ridiculous, she told herself crossly as she changed slacks and a T-shirt for a sun-dress which would be more comfortable. True, Clint Dubois was different from any man she had met, but in her twenty-four years she should have learned to conduct herself with all manner of people without getting herself into a flurry of nerves.

When she came down the stairs she saw that he was waiting for her. The door was open, and he was looking over the valley. The wide shoulders were rigid, and she wondered if he was already regretting his invitation.

She said hesitantly, 'Mr Dubois....'

He spun round, and she saw that she had not imagined his impatience. He looked down at her, his eyes narrowing as he took in her appearance, from smooth shoulders which were revealed by the narrow straps of the sundress, to small well-shaped feet in thonged sandals.

She felt tension rising inside her at the blatancy of his scrutiny. 'Yes,' she said defiantly, as if in answer to an unspoken challenge, 'I *did* get changed. I'm sorry if you don't approve.'

His head came up slowly, and in his eyes was an expression which she had never seen there before and couldn't define.

'What makes you think,' drawled Clint Dubois, 'that I don't approve?'

There was something in his tone which left her feeling as if she had been stripped naked. An angry retort sprang to her lips, but at the last moment she managed to check it. No point in fighting with the man, she reminded herself. While she needed his employment she must try to keep the peace. 'Thank you,' she murmured, hoping that the spots of colour in her cheeks did not give the lie to her demure manner.

They would be making a very general tour of the estate, Clint said as they walked together down the wide stone steps. It was impossible to cover the finer details in a short time, but Jana would be able to get some understanding of the architecture and layout which made Devil's View so well known. Jana tried to concentrate on his words, but it was hard, for his voice seemed to be coming to her from a distance, a distance that had nothing to do with the height which made him tower above her. The difficulty had more to do with the fact that she was too achingly aware of the man at her side to be able to take in what he was saying.

It came to her quite suddenly that the flow of

explanation had stopped. She lifted her head to find
him watching her, his expression questioning, as if
he was waiting for an answer to something he had
said.

'It ... it's very beautiful.' The words stumbled
out hesitantly.

'It is,' he agreed pleasantly. 'Perhaps you'd like
to make some notes at this point?'

'Notes?' Her voice was low and uncertain.

'Regarding the history of the east gable.'

'I. ... Yes, of course'

She bent her head, and fumbled in her purse for
her pen. The hand that caught her chin took her
unawares, causing the breath to jerk from her lungs.
The fingers were lean and strong, tilting her face
up without any effort.

'You haven't heard a word I've been saying.'
There was an enigmatic quality in the accusation.
'What were you thinking?'

She couldn't tell him the truth: it was too shocking to admit even to herself. So she said the next
thing that came to mind. 'What it would be like
for a child to play on these lawns.'

His hand dropped abruptly to his side. The
gentleness which had momentarily softened the
stern features vanished, to be replaced by an uncompromising hardness. 'You are no less subtle than
all the others of your sex,' he said harshly.

She was trembling as she stared up at him. His
lips were a tight line, his eyes chips of ice. What
had she said to provoke such anger?

'I don't understand. . . .' she began nervously, her pink tongue going out to moisten dry lips.

'How well you play the part of the simple maiden,' he mocked her.

She could feel the tears pricking at her eyelids, but she blinked them away as anger began to rise inside her. Whatever she had said to annoy him, it had been unintentional. He might be her employer, but that did not give him the right to speak to her in this arrogant fashion. 'The least you could do is tell me what I said wrong.'

'As if you didn't know!' The arrogant mockery she so hated was intensified. 'Children playing on the lawn. The sound of laughter ringing through the empty rooms. That would have been the next remark. Do you really think I'm taken in by all those feminine remarks?' A harsh laugh. 'I'll say this—you're more brazen than most.'

'Brazen?' she echoed in astonishment.

'Brazen,' he repeated with a taunt. 'When did you decide that you wanted to be mistress of Devil's View?'

# CHAPTER FIVE

She stared at him speechlessly. For a moment she wondered if he was joking, but the implacability of his expression indicated that he had meant every word.

'Well, Miss Harvey,' he went on relentlessly, 'when *did* you make your decision? Was it when you came here to apply for the job? Or was it earlier, when you put on your drowning act at Fish Hoek?'

The dark eyes that seemed to savage her whole being were chips of ice. Knowing only that she did not want him to see the tears threatening beneath her lids, she turned her back on him. Her chest was tight with pain, and once again it came to her that in his past there had been a woman who had hurt him so deeply that thenceforth all other women became suspect.

She was unprepared for the hands that seized her shoulders and spun her round to face him. Unsuccessfully she tried to wrench away from his grip.

'Take your hands off me!' she hissed through her pain.

'So now it's the outraged virgin bit,' he mocked her. 'Really, Miss Harvey, don't you think you could at least try to be consistent?'

'What ... what do you mean?' she whispered.

'You weren't averse to my touch on that first day.'

'I didn't know you then,' she said evenly. 'Besides, I didn't ask you to rescue me.'

'No?' Again the mockery which she loathed. 'That is debatable, isn't it?' He paused, and she saw the mirthless smile which lifted the corners of his mouth. 'When the danger had passed and I was holding you, you didn't seem to mind. In fact,'— his tone became an insolent drawl—'I'd say that you enjoyed it.'

There was no point in denying the latter part of the accusation. He was too perceptive a man not to have sensed the way she had come alive at his touch. She said simply, 'I didn't know you then.'

'Assuming you're telling the truth—which I doubt—you recognised me when you came for the interview. You also agreed to the conditions of employment. So you knew very well what to expect.'

'And what was that?' she asked, a little breathlessly.

'This.'

The hands that held her shoulders tightened as they slid down her back. There was nothing tender in his kiss. His lips were brutal, punishing. She tried to twist away from him, but the movement had the reverse effect; it made him draw her even closer against him. Strong as he was, she did not stop fighting him. Her mind was outraged at the brutality of his behaviour. And yet, in complete contradiction, her senses were leaping with an excitement that was unbearable.

He lifted his head, as if to draw breath, and his hold released slightly. In that moment she managed to pull away. Now she did not think rationally There was only instinct. She lifted her hand and slapped him hard across the face.

She heard his swift intake of breath. A hand went to his cheek, then back to her, as if to pull her to him again. This time she was too swift for him. She took a step backwards, crouching like a wounded animal as she stared up at him.

'You little vixen!' It was almost a snarl.

'You dare say that after the way you behaved!' Her eyes were blazing, her self-control almost gone, torn not only by the outrage he had inflicted on her, but even more by her own reaction to it. Dimly she knew that there was a part of her which had revelled in his brutality, even while she had rebelled against it. It was a flash of self-knowledge which was totally unacceptable.

He looked down at her for a long moment. His eyes were hooded, his expression undefinable. 'All I did was to give you what you expected,' he said at last, and his tone was remote.

'How dare you!' It was not in her to match his detachment, not when her emotions and her senses were in a turmoil she had never before experienced. It took an almost superhuman effort to keep a sob from her voice, but she managed it. Her limbs were weak, but she stood very straight and in her face was a look of pride and defiance. 'Whatever you may think, Mr Dubois, I am not a tart.'

'No?' His hand reached for her throat, trailing lightly, sensuously, along the slender column to the tiny hollow where the rapid pulse showed her tension.

'No,' she said firmly. 'For the last time—I did not plan to be rescued. Nor did I know that you were the owner of Devil's View.'

Green eyes were steady as they looked up at him. His own eyes were narrowed and hard as they studied the small oval face, the heightened colour in the soft cheeks, the trembling lips. As he took his hand from her throat—absurd how she missed the touch!—the mockery was gone from his lips.

When he spoke his tone was quiet, but with no hint of apology in it. 'I believe you,' he said.

She turned away, so that he would not see the hot tears which scalded her eyes. But his next words had her spinning round to face him.

'I still think you're playing at something.'

'Why?' she asked numbly.

'You say you're researching Cape Dutch architecture.'

'Yes....' She was wary now, wondering what was coming.

'You must have done some research before coming here.'

'.... Of course.'

'That's odd.' His words were measured. 'I had the strangest feeling that my explanations while we were walking had very little relevance for you.'

'Because I spoke of children?'

'Not only that.' His eyes were gleaming. Malice? she wondered, bracing herself for a new onslaught of sarcasm. 'Why weren't you taking notes, Miss Harvey? You made a point of bringing pen and paper.'

'It isn't always necessary to write things down.' She tried to speak calmly. 'I ... I have a good memory.'

'Let's put it to the test.'

She swallowed. 'Is that necessary?'

A dangerous smile sketched the mobile lips. 'To satisfy my curiosity—yes.'

'I wasn't aware that this would be included in my duties.' Her voice was tight. 'But if it's what you want....'

'I do. Tell me the name of the architect who designed Devil's View.' The words were said so mildly that they were hardly in the form of a question, but the steady gaze left no doubt that an answer was expected.

Desperately she searched her mind. Had he mentioned a name? Vaguely she thought that he had. Damn Clint Dubois! He had no right to put her through this ordeal.

'Well?' He was waiting. He stood a few steps away from her, lean fingers hooked casually in the waistband of well-cut trousers. His whole stance was relaxed and casual. But there was nothing relaxed in the eyes that watched her so intently.

'Would you believe it?' She managed a light laugh. 'The name is on the tip of my tongue, and for the life of me I can't think of it.'

'Is that so?' A sardonic drawl.

'Ridiculous, isn't it?' Her voice was rising. 'I mean, I know so much about his work, and.... It's just his name that escapes me.'

'Louis Thibault,' he supplied.

'Louis Thibault! Of course!' Another laugh.

'Of course.' His tone was very mild, very soft. She looked at him swiftly. He was smiling, a gentle smile, with a hint of seductiveness, and she thought of a cat playing with a mouse, baiting the helpless creature until it was ready to pounce. For a few moments there was absolute stillness, a stillness that made the buzzing of a bee on a nearby shrub seem unnaturally loud.

Then he said, 'And of course you know the name of the sculptor Thibault worked with.'

Jana battled to stem the hysteria rising within her. 'Actually I don't,' she admitted, with a calmness that surprised her.

'Impossible!' An eyebrow lifted in pretended surprise. 'They did so much work together.'

'Gilbert and Sullivan,' she said with wry humour.

'Exactly. Know Louis Thibault and you know Anton Anreith.' A flash of white strong teeth in the lean tanned face as he grinned. 'But of course, Anreith's name was there with Thibault's, right on the tip of that delectable little pink tongue.'

'Mr Dubois!' Her colour was high.

'Yes, Miss Harvey.' The rugged face was complacent. 'I'm a heel to mention your tongue. Just as I'm a heel to go on about an architect and a sculptor you'd never heard of in your life.' Another flash of white teeth. 'But I think I've made my point?'

What did the mouse do once it was caught? Allow the cat to torment it unmercifully until it grew tired of its game? Or did it make an effort, futile though it might be, to wriggle free?

A small pointed chin lifted defiantly, and green eyes sparkled with the light of battle. 'I'm not after your silver, if that's what you think,' she challenged him.

He chuckled, and for once he sounded genuinely amused. 'How reassuring to know that you're not a thief!'

The colour came and went in her cheeks. A thief she was not, but her quest would involve a thorough search of the house, and the thought of what he might do if he caught her at it was frightening.

She became aware that he was watching her. The change of colour had not passed unnoticed. She hoped that she had not given him any foolish ideas. If he were to engage someone to watch her movements the search would become impossible.

'Nor am I out to be mistress of Devil's View.' Spiritedly she changed direction.

'Just as well—because it takes two to make that sort of commitment.'

It was a warning, quietly spoken and with the outward trappings of humour—but a warning all the same. There was a small ache in her chest. Any mistress of Devil's View would have to be Clint Dubois's wife, and nothing was further from Jana's mind. It therefore came to her with a sense of shock that his quiet warning had the power to hurt her.

With her eyes on the ground she was unprepared for the hand that drew her chin up once more. Shivers of awareness tingled down her spine as she was forced to look into the enigmatic face so close to hers.

'While we're on the subject—why are you not married, Jana?'

Her heart thumped violently at the unexpected use of her first name. She tried to look away from him but, as if his will was greater than hers, she found that she could not.

'That's a ridiculous question.' The words came from a parched throat.

'Not when it's put to a young and beautiful and very desirable woman.' One finger had begun a stroking movement, slow and sensual, igniting flickers of flame through her whole being.

'You find me desirable?' The question emerged entirely without volition.

There was a darkening in the grey eyes. 'Asking me to prove it to you again?'

'No!' She shook her head violently. It was as if she was denying even to herself the need to feel his arms around her once more. 'But if ... you do ... find me desirable, why do you dislike me so much?'

She saw the tightening of a muscle in the lean

jaw, the narrowing of his eyes. 'My dear Jana, you can't have gone this far in life without discovering that sex-appeal and affection don't necessarily go hand in hand.'

She flinched, just as if he had hurt her physically. 'You really hate me, don't you?' she asked with difficulty.

'Now you're being melodramatic.' His tone was impersonal. The thumb stopped its stroking movement, and she was glad, for the movement was so sensuous that she thought she would go mad. 'Distrust is more like it.'

'Because I don't know as much about Cape Dutch architecture as you thought I would?'

His eyes flicked her face impassively. 'If you want to be specific. But in general—I have no great trust in your sex, Miss Harvey.'

So it was back to formality. She took a deep breath. 'Perhaps you'd like me to leave Devil's View, Mr Dubois?' She knew the implication of her question even as she asked it. If she could not go on with the search Simon would be upset. But at this moment what Simon thought about the matter did not seem important.

Clint laughed softly, and she could feel his warm breath on her cheek. 'Did I say that?'

'You implied it.'

'I merely expressed my distrust.' He shrugged. 'I need a secretary. You can spell and your typing is accurate—qualities not easily come by these days. As for you, for reasons of your own, you want to be at Devil's View.' A flash of the wicked grin which was becoming heart-stoppingly familiar. 'The situation seems to suit us both.'

He stepped away from her then. The discourse on the history of Devil's View had come to an abrupt end. Jana did not refer to it, and Clint Dubois seemed to have decided that any further explanations on his part were a waste of his time. At a fork in the path they parted. There was machinery he wanted to inspect in the cellars, he told Jana. He did not invite her to join him.

Dinner was a bleak and silent meal. The food was good—fresh Cape sole baked in wine sauce, followed by a crisp apple tart with whipped cream—but Jana had so little appetite that it could all just as well have been cardboard. She would have liked to push the plate away, but Clint's domineering presence forced her to a pretence of eating. There was virtually no conversation between them. Jana's mind was empty of subjects, and it appeared that Clint was not the man to make meaningless small-talk.

Once, thinking herself unobserved, Jana stole a glance at him. In contrast to her own tension, he looked relaxed and at ease. His face, tanned and lean and finely-chiselled, wore an air of remoteness, leading Jana to wonder whether he had forgotten her presence at the table.

Quite suddenly he turned his head. He did not speak, but the eyes that met hers were sardonic and mocking, and Jana's heart thumped painfully as she dropped her eyes back to her food. He knows exactly what he's doing to me, she thought angrily. He knows, and he derives pleasure from it.

Dinner over, Clint stood up and with a curt good-night he left the room. Jana would have given much to know his plans for the evening. She sat a while longer at the table, sipping at a second cup of coffee, waiting to hear the sound of a car. If he would only go out she would have the house to herself. But all was quiet.

With a sigh she put down her cup and left the dining-room. Passing the library, she paused. The door was closed. Was Clint in there? What did he do with himself in the evenings? He could be reading or working. It did not really matter what he was doing; with Clint in the house she could not move around freely. All she could do was search in her own bedroom.

She had already made a start. Now she looked around the lovely room with its brocaded pink bed-spread and the heavy matching curtains, with the furniture that glowed from years of polishing and care, and wondered why she didn't feel more enthusiastic. With no definite idea where to look, it was obvious that she must begin with one wall and work her way methodically around the room. For a while she pressed her hands against the panelling, stopping every moment or two to listen for the sound of a hollow cavity, but it was dreary work and for some reason she did not have her heart in it.

She had worked her way around the room without finding anything. Clearly she must extend her search elsewhere, and the idea filled her with despondency. She had seen already how many rooms were involved. Also, she was beginning to realise that time was limited. It was not often that the house was empty. During the day the staff were busy with housework. That left only the evenings—and as yet it was not apparent how often Clint Dubois went out.

She toyed for a few minutes with the idea of trying one of the other rooms, then abandoned it as being too dangerous. Already her employer suspected her motives for coming to Devil's View. If he caught her in a room where she had no right to be, there was no gauging his reaction.

She picked up a book and tried to read, but when she had read the same page three times, and the words still remained meaningless, she slipped on a cardigan and went outside.

It was a summer evening, warm and lovely. Above her towered the mountain, a dark and impenetrable mass. Ribbons of light weaved along the shore-front, and far out at sea she could see the tiny lights of distant ships. The spicy smell of the pines mingled with the scents of the rock plants that grew here in such profusion—proteas and aloes and deep scarlet fuchsias. A moon hung in the sky, almost full, and its light gilded the house and the ground with an ethereal radiance.

Sitting down on a rock Jana stared at the house

which had once been her home, and was now her home again temporarily in circumstances which were becoming rapidly more disturbing. Earlier that afternoon Clint had talked in technical terms of mouldings and gables, of dates and styles of architecture, but most of, it had been lost on her. Jana knew very little of architecture, and she understood now how foolish it had been to pretend to something which could be seen through quite easily by a knowledgeable person.

But if the house meant nothing to her in terms of style and period, in another sense it was beginning to mean more and more. Robed in its sheen of golden moonlight, Jana thought it looked like something out of a fairy-tale. The windows had been closed against the night, and the shutters folded. It was mysterious and secretive, and at the same time incredibly lovely. There was the graceful curve of the gable, and the lacelike tracery of metal fencing. There were the wooden beams with their tumble of creepers, dancing shadows against the pale walls.

Jana's home in Johannesburg was an apartment in a tall modern building, a building without a past. In contrast, Devil's View had a past which stretched back two hundred years to a time when Table Bay had been little more than a trading station for the Dutch East India Company, and when the modern city of Cape Town had been no more than a dream. Devil's View was a house with tradition, with history, a house where generations of families had lived and loved and died; a house with secrets.

Somewhere within those walls lay the secret to Jana's own past. But she was beginning to despair that she would ever find it.

It was becoming obvious that the search could take weeks—and then the finding might be a matter of luck. But for Simon's insistence Jana would have been content to leave the past to itself.

Not for the first time she wondered whether she had been foolish to let Simon and his mother talk her into this quest. Such had been their kindness and hospitality that it had seemed churlish to refuse, even when she did not entirely agree with their reasoning. Seen from the distance of Johannesburg, and with no understanding of the place she was coming to, the search had appeared simple enough. Now she knew differently, and she could not help the faint stirrings of resentment.

It was three days since Jana had spoken to Simon. True, she had not wanted to phone him from Devil's View, and she had not been back to the inn to ask if she could use the telephone there. But Simon knew where she was. Had he wanted to, he could have got hold of her. . . . Impatiently she shrugged a swathe of hair from her shoulders. This line of thinking could only lead one way. She was letting her uneasiness get the better of her. Next she would begin to doubt Simon's love for her—and that would never do.

She had always tried to be honest with herself. As she sat on her rock in the darkness, drinking in the unearthly moonlit beauty that was Devil's View, she knew that the search was only one reason for her uneasiness. She could no longer deny to herself that the owner of Devil's View as the greatest cause of her tension. Right from the start, when he had rescued her from the whirlpool and had held her body against his, she had been acutely aware of him. Clint Dubois was like no man she had ever known. Certainly nobody else had ever made such an impact on her senses.

She must get away from Devil's View. It was imperative that she get away from the man whose personality was beginning to corrode her deepest emotions, who was awakening a part of her that was so primitive and primeaval that she had never known it existed. His attraction was undoubted but it was purely physical. She could never feel for him the kind of love that she felt for Simon. That was impossible. Yet for her own peace of mind it was important that she sever all contact with him.

No matter whether Simon's reasons for wanting her to delve into the past were valid. He would have to agree that she abandon the whole affair. Simon was not without faults, but he was gentle, caring. When he understood that she was unhappy he would urge her to leave Devil's View and catch the next plane to Johannesburg.

Ideally she should phone him now. But it was dark, and she was not yet familiar with the twists and turns of the mountain road. After lunch tomorrow she would find an opportunity to slip away from the house. She would phone him then.

Of course, she would have to give Clint notice. Even after three days she could not just vanish like a thief in the night. A week would be sufficient; that was what they had agreed on. He would not be surprised. Other secretaries had left him, and so far he had always managed to find a replacement.

No, Clint Dubois would not be surprised. Nor would he care. Curiously, the knowledge hurt.

Clint was waiting for her when she came into her office the next morning. He was standing against a filing cabinet, one long leg stretched over the other, as he leaned back reading. His dark hair was wind-ruffled, and the skin of his face glowed beneath the tan. A pale blue shirt moulded the broad chest, an attractive contrast with the well-cut navy trousers. Jana had not expected him so early, and as she walked to her desk she could not stop the sudden racing of her heart, nor her accountable surge of pleasure at the sight of him.

'You're late.' He did not look up from his reading.

The happiness faded. 'I understood that I began at nine. . . .'

'It's three minutes after.'

'I'm sorry. It's such a glorious morning that I thought I'd walk in the garden a while.' She bit her lip uncertainly.

'I expect you to be on time.' His voice was cold.

Anger rose inside her at his arrogance. 'Do a few

minutes matter so much?' she questioned defiantly.

His head lifted. Grey eyes swept her from head to foot in a glance that was a deliberate insult. 'This is an office, Miss Harvey. We keep office hours. Don't forget it.'

'No wonder you can't keep a secretary,' she tossed at him. 'Nobody could stand your arrogance!'

'You're being paid to stand it,' he reminded her crisply. 'Get your notebook and pencil.'

She stared at him, the small oval face a study in outrage. Her lips parted, but before she could tell him what she thought of him a hand seized her wrist in an iron grip, and she felt herself being forced into her seat.

'We'll have a discourse on my insufferable personality some other time.' His face was taut with impatience. 'There's a lot of work to get through today.'

Only will-power stilled the trembling of her fingers as she took her note pad and pencil from a drawer. She kept her eyes concealed beneath long-lashed lids and waited for him to begin dictating. Not for anything would she let him see how much his manner affected her. If it was only anger she felt, it would not matter. In fact it would do him good to know that his high-handedness had prompted her hatred. But even stronger than anger was a mixture of sorrow and disappointment that he should be quite so indifferent to her as a person.

He was riffling through a bundle of papers, and she managed to steal a quick glance at him. Everything about him indicated power and authority; the wide brow that was furrowed in a slight frown, the firm set of the lips, the long strong line of the jaw. His dictation was as efficient as everything else about him; crisp, terse and to the point. There was no fumbling for words, no hesitation. He seemed to have all the facts and figures of the vast wine estate at his finger-tips. Despite her dislike of Clint Dubois as a person, Jana could not help a feeling of admiration. It was easy to see why the vineyards of Devil's View, famous even before Clint took them over, had become even more lucrative in recent years.

He had finished dictating and was about to leave the office when Jana, possessed of sudden daring, murmured, 'I'll eat in my room from now on, Mr Dubois.'

He turned and looked at her over his shoulder. There was a sardonic expression in the brief glance he gave her. 'You know my orders.'

She coloured angrily, resenting his arrogance. 'I would prefer to eat alone.'

'I will not have my staff put to extra trouble.' His voice was mild, but with a razor-sharp edge to it. 'I'll see you at one in the dining-room, Miss Harvey.' He left the room without a backward glance.

# CHAPTER SIX

SEVERAL minutes elapsed before Jana regained enough composure to begin work. The interchange had lasted no more than a few seconds, but it seemed that any contact with the man who was her employer was enough to put emotions in turmoil. Once more she was distressed that her primary reaction was not one of anger, though anger existed—it was a natural reaction in the circumstances. What was decidedly unnatural was the flame of excitement shivering through her system. It made the call to Simon more important than ever.

But first there was work to do. She could not slip away from the house and risk Clint's wrath if he came into the office and saw that she had gone out without finishing all the correspondence. Lifting the cover from the typewriter, she took a few deep steadying breaths, and began to type.

Despite her annoyance with Clint Dubois, she soon found herself absorbed in her work. She had never realised how much was involved in the running of a big wine estate. Perhaps, before she left Devil's View for Johannesburg, she would even get a glimpse of the wineries themselves....

She did not hear the door open. When a feminine voice said, 'Well, if it isn't the industrious Miss

Harvey!' she jerked her head up sharply.

The sight of glossy black hair and deep blue eyes was familiar, but in her confusion Jana could not think where she had seen the girl.

'Miranda Maddison.' The information was supplied with a disdainful smile. 'We met at Fish Hoek.'

Miranda! The girl who had shown her dislike after the rescue.... 'Of course.' Jana forced a polite smile, as she was swept by recognition. 'I'm sorry I didn't recognise you.'

'Small wonder you didn't remember me. You only had eyes for Clint, didn't you?' Hostility gleamed in the lovely eyes.

Jana had to stifle a gasp at the blatant rudeness of the remark. Her voice cold, she said, 'If you remember, I'd had a shock.'

'So you're still holding on to that story?' A shrill laugh. 'I must hand it to you—when you set out to accomplish something you certainly go for novelty!'

It was bad enough that she must convince her employer that the near-drowning was an accident. To have to make explanations to this voluptuous girl with the ice-blue eyes was unthinkable. Jana kept her silence and waited.

'Don't you think you were being rather obvious?' asked Miranda.

'Obvious?' Jana repeated carefully.

'I mean, coming up here to Devil's View to coax Clint into taking you on the very day after you'd compromised him on the beach.'

Jana took a deep breath. 'It was pure coincidence. Not that I expect you to believe it.' She looked pointedly at the door. 'You'll have to excuse me. Mr Dubois is expecting these letters to be finished.'

'Mr Dubois, is it? How very formal!' The shrill voice was mocking. 'And it had better stay that way.' Miranda bent closer. 'Understand one thing, Miss Harvey—Clint Dubois is mine.'

A small tremor slid through Jana's nerve-stream. Outwardly she remained composed. 'Mr Dubois doesn't strike me as being the kind of person who would belong to anybody.'

'Don't play games with me.' The words spat out venomously. 'Clint and I are going to be married. And if you try to get in my way you'll be sorry.'

With an almost superhuman effort Jana inserted a fresh sheet into the typewriter. Her eyes were on the notes in her shorthand-pad, where Miranda could not see the devastating emotion she had aroused with her statement. Her heart was pounding painfully, and her throat seemed to have gone so dry that she wondered if she would be able to speak.

'You *do* understand?' Miranda's voice cut the air like a knife.

'Your personal affairs don't concern me.' Jana's voice was low.

'Well, just as long as you understand. No more coincidences or. . . .'

'Coincidence?' drawled a familiar voice, bringing both girls spinning round to look at him.

Miranda was the first to recover. She threw him an artless smile. 'We were having such an interesting discussion—all about life and coincidence.' There was nothing in her expression to suggest that she was at all put out by Clint's sudden appearance. Jana could not help a grudging admiration.

'I'm sorry I missed it.' Clint's voice was dry, but there was a gleam in his eyes and Jana had the feeling that he was amused.

'You're teasing me.' A tinkling laugh as Miranda looked at him with a flirtatious archness that made Jana feel sick. 'You didn't forget I was coming to have lunch with you, darling?'

Despite what Miranda had said about their impending marriage, the use of the endearment sent a new emotion scorching through Jana. Horrified, she had just identified it as jealousy when Clint said, 'We can eat now.' He inclined his head towards Jana. 'If you're ready, Miss Harvey?'

'I'd counted on being alone with you, darling.' Miranda's hand was on his arm, and the rosebud mouth was pouting. 'You said you had a pile of work to do, Miss Harvey.'

'That's so,' Jana acknowledged, a little too quickly. 'I think I'll just have a tray sent in here, Mr Dubois.'

'I thought we'd settled that issue.' There was a ring of authority in Clint's tone so that even Miranda kept silent. 'I will not have the staff put to extra work. You will join us, Miss Harvey.'

I shall choke, Jana thought, the flash of self-revelation which she still did not quite understand like bile in her throat. I can't sit there calmly and eat while you and your wife-to-be whisper sweet nothings at each other.

But it seemed there was nothing for it. Clint remained firm despite Miranda's pouting. The other girl's sulkiness gave Jana a slight sense of satisfaction. Miranda's hostility had provoked in her an unprecedented feeling of dislike. Any discomfort she might feel in the dining-room would be lessened by the knowledge that Miranda resented her presence.

Despite her outward show of composure at the dining-room table, Jana felt strained and ill at ease. Miranda kept up a constant stream of chatter, brittle and light and mainly inconsequential, and all of it directed at Clint. Jana might not have existed. Clint's replies were brief, but never rude, Jana noted, and lacking in the arrogance he used with Jana herself. From the conversation it emerged that Miranda was a neighbour and a model, that her father was a wealthy man who would one day confer all he had upon his adored only daughter.

No wonder that Clint was interested in her. Self-sufficient he might be, arrogant and tough and sure of his power over women; yet it seemed that he was not above the temptation of marriage with a woman who was not only beautiful, but who also had enough money to make up any shortfall he might need for the enhancement of his estate.

If it was easy to understand Clint's interest in Miranda, it was harder for Jana to accept it. Her new feelings were something she would have to understand before she could fight them. They did not make sense. She was engaged to be married herself, to a man who was in every way a more worthwhile person than Clint Dubois. Any feelings of jealousy—it was hard to deny the emotion for what it was—could only be a case of sour grapes. She did not want the man herself. Despite his undoubted physical attraction she did not even like him. She shied away from the word 'love'.... If she resented the idea that Clint was interested in another woman it could only be that after the few days of enforced proximity her vanity was hurt by the fact that he showed no interest at all in herself. All perfectly logical. And none of it quite true, Jana acknowledged with despair.

The meal over, she watched Miranda and Clint leave the room together. A well-groomed hand was tucked possessively through a bronzed arm, and dark curls brushed his shoulder as Miranda laughed up at him. As their voices faded and Jana wondered where they were going, she felt pain knotting in her chest.

Slowly she made her way back to the little office with its lovely view over the garden. For once the peacefulness of the room was lost on her. On her desk was a pile of letters which must be ready before the day ended, but Jana found herself incapable of making a start. She went to the window and opened it wide. Thoughtfully she stared over the lawns and shrubs to the purple vista of vineyards. She knew she must get back to her work, but she knew too that she must come to terms with her own thoughts first.

She could no longer shrug away the awareness that swamped her whenever she saw her employer. For all the arrogance and self-confidence which she detested, there was something about the man which she was beginning to find ever more attractive. It was a quality which made her feel vibrant and young and alive. Until now she had prided herself on her independence, on the fact that she was able to handle herself competently in a man's world. What was it about Clint Dubois that made her feel utterly feminine? Why did she have the desire— an utterly crazy desire in the light of her engagement to another man—to know that her employer thought of her as a woman?

It was not enough that he should esteem her because she could spell and had the ability to type accurately. She wanted him to think of her as beautiful and feminine and desirable. She wanted it more than anything else. Beautiful and desirable— they were words he had said to her once. But he had spoken in derision, after kissing her in a manner that left her in no doubt that all he wanted was to show his power and contempt.

She already knew it was jealousy she had experienced earlier, when she had watched him walk away with Miranda Maddison. A primitive and consuming jealousy. But why, why, why? She did not love him. He had all the qualities she most loathed in a man. Besides, she was in love with Simon....

If only she could forget the moments she had spent in his arms! By day she was able, albeit with a deliberate effort, to push them from her mind. But at night, when she slept, she was powerless to control her dreams. And on waking, when her mind was still hazy, images would come without volition. It was then that memory was most vivid, so that she would feel again the touch and taste of his lips, the strength of his arms, the power of the long muscled thighs.

Clint Dubois could stir her. No doubt he could stir any woman. And she, Jana Harvey, was reacting like a star-struck teenager. Where was her pride? she asked herself with a touch of despair. What had happened to her common sense? Was she utterly mad to let herself be carried away by dreams of a stranger with whom there was not the slightest possibility of a future?

And why this unreasonable jealousy of Miranda? True, she did not like the girl, but there was no reason in the world why Clint should share her feelings. Miranda was rich and pretty. No doubt she would project a gracious and radiant image when she was mistress of Devil's View. Clint's wife.... She forced herself to say the words aloud, as if to make the concept positive in her mind. But she felt no happier for it. Miranda Maddison was a butterfly, a calculating woman who wanted Clint because he could give her all the good things in life that she desired.

Would Jana feel differently about any other woman whom Clint might choose to marry? Yes, said her brain. No, insisted her heart.

With a jerky movement she spun from the window and stared blindly into the room. Her heart was fluttering unevenly, and she could feel the blood draining from her cheeks. Simon.... She closed her eyes and tried to bring a picture of him into her mind. It was only after moments, and then with difficulty, that she was able to summon sufficient of his features to give the image any kind of meaning. There was the square dimpled chin, the laughing eyes, the sensitive mouth, the crooked boyish smile, all of which were so appealing. She had him now, the Simon she knew and loved. And yet, somehow, it was an image without any substance.

The madness had progressed further than she had realised. All day she had planned on phoning Simon. Now more than ever she must speak to him. If she heard his voice, the distance between them would vanish, and he would assume his erstwhile reality. A reality which she would henceforth cling to with grim doggedness. At the same time she would avoid Clint Dubois. For the time she remained at Devil's View—and that time must be as short as she could make it—she would maintain a deliberate aloofness. He would not have the opportunity to dizzy her mind and senses again.

Clint and Miranda were nowhere to be seen as Jana left the house and went to the garage. She had left her work untouched. Briefly she wondered if Clint would be angry. But she would be back in no time, and if he was as occupied with Miranda as Jana supposed, then he would not even know she had been away. At the worst, she would have to endure his anger. For her own peace of mind she must get her priorities straight. Right now there was nothing more important than that she should speak to Simon.

The innkeeper was glad to see her. 'You'll be wanting to use the phone, miss?'

'Please....'

'Jana, honey,' Simon sounded curiously disembodied. 'You've found it?'

No exclamation of joy at hearing her voice. No outpourings of how much he was missing her. Just that faint voice from a million miles away asking if she had found something that was beginning to mean less and less. Disappointment made her feel limp and a little cold. 'Not yet,' she said.

'Honey, this is taking ages.' His tone was accusing.

'The way it's going it could take forever.' She paused, then said flatly, 'If I find it at all.'

'But Jana....' He was taken aback. 'You always said....'

'My grandmother said it,' she interrupted crisply. 'Simon, do you realise that I don't know what exactly I'm looking for? I don't know where to look. Devil's View has a great many rooms, and every one of them is panelled.'

There was a moment of silence. When Simon spoke again he sounded disgruntled. 'Where does that leave things?'

Jana hesitated. Then she took a deep breath. 'That depends on you.'

Silence. Her words must have made an impact on him, Jana thought with a slight touch of malice. It was unlike Simon to let the seconds tick away like this, second by expensive second.

When he spoke his voice was abrupt. 'You'd better come back.'

'You want me to abandon the search?'

So much depended on his answer. The knowledge that he loved her enough to pit that love against his mother's anger and the name of the firm. Reassurance that she could dispense with the niggling doubts which were worrying her more and more of late. The relief of knowing that her future with Simon was secure.

It seemed that a whole lifetime hinged on his words. How strange, that while she waited for him to speak, she was aware only of the familiar ache beneath her ribs.

'When can you get back?'

It was only later that Jana was to realise that

he had evaded her question. 'I ... I'm not certain.' Her hand tightened on the receiver, as if
she was afraid of dropping it.

'You'll catch the next plane, of course,' he
ordered.

Something stirred inside her at the terseness of
the command. 'I have a job,' she reminded him.

'A façade.' He was impatient.

'Not to Mr Dubois,' she said breathlessly. And
not to me either. Another moment of revelation.

'You're not committed to the man,' came the
disembodied voice.

I wish that I was. The thought had flashed
through her mind before she could stop it. Shaking now, her hand tightened on the receiver, as if
she was afraid of dropping it. 'I'll have to give him
notice.'

'Twenty-four hours?'

'A week.'

'For heaven's sake, Jana!' He barked the words
into the phone, and Jana flinched.

'It's what we arranged. . . .'

'Walk out on him.' Strange, Jana thought, that
she had never before noticed the arrogance in him.
It was a different arrogance from her employer's.
She put her free hand to her head. Why was she
making comparisons? 'You wouldn't be the first,'
Simon was saying.

'I owe Mr Dubois some loyalty.' She said it very
clearly.

Another short silence. This time, when Simon spoke, she detected a difference in his tone. 'This fellow you're living with....'

'I work with him,' she corrected him icily.

'Naturally,' he said, and she wondered briefly what was so natural about the whole set-up. 'I wasn't insinuating anything.'

'No?' She dropped the word idly. Abstractedly she studied her left hand. It seemed a long time since the ring had been on her fourth finger.

'No!' There was a short bark of unamused laughter at the other end of the line. 'You're just trying to provoke me. It's obvious that you wouldn't get up to anything with another man.'

'You're very sure of me.' She couldn't seem to stop.

'Of course. I mean....' There was sudden uncertainty in his tone. 'I've never known you like this. Look, honey, has something happened?'

'No,' she told him very softly. 'Nothing at all.'

'Well.... Jana, honey, you feel very strongly about having to give notice?'

'Very.'

'In that case ... I want you to move into a hotel.' His tone became aggressive. 'I will *not* have my fiancée living alone in a house with another man.'

Which was what he should have said at the very beginning, she thought wryly, when the fruitless search had begun. Clint Dubois would not have agreed to the arrangement, and Simon would have been forced to make a decision on the matter of the search then. The time at Devil's View had wrought a change in Jana. She knew that her feelings for Simon would never be quite the same again.

'Jana, listen to me. I want you to move out of Devil's View today. Let me know when you've booked your plane. I'll be at the airport to meet you.'

This time she did not ask if he loved her. They said their goodbyes briefly, swiftly. When Jana put down the phone she was still trembling.

She was walking away from the phone when she felt a hand on her arm. She kept her head down a moment before she turned to the innkeeper, not wanting him to see the tears that stood on her lashes.

'Bad news?' he questioned with perception.

She shook her head, and tried to smile.

'Miss Harvey,' he began, and she saw that he was uncomfortable, as if there was something he wanted to say, and was searching for a way to be tactful. 'There's talk around here.... You understand, I'm just telling you this because I don't want to see you hurt.'

'What kind of talk?'

'About you ... and Mr Dubois....'

It was what she had expected when she'd noticed his uneasiness, but she could not help being curious. 'I don't know why there should be,' she said slowly. 'I'm not the first secretary who's lived at Devil's View.'

'People say you're different. . . . That there's something between the two of you.'

If only there were! Again the flash of self-revelation, tingling through her like an electric shock. She did not need to ask who was responsible for the gossip. It could only be Miranda Maddison.

'It's nonsense,' she said. 'Please believe me.'

The old face creased in a smile of relief. 'I do believe you. I just want to be sure you weren't being hurt.' His lips tightened. 'Next person who says anything, I'll know how to put them right.'

Despite her eagerness to be at her desk before Clint missed her, Jana drove back slowly. The stretch of road leading from the inn to Devil's View was steep and winding, and she had learned to treat its bends with respect. It was also very beautiful, so beautiful that Jana thought sometimes that she could never grow tired of it. The sun was slanting through the silver trees, tingeing the leaves and bark with a translucent radiance. Flowers grew at the roadside. There were lupins and tiny white and yellow mountain blossoms, and here and there a protea or an aloe with glossy leaves and spiky-edged blooms. Mist covered the top of Table Mountain, but Devil's Peak and Lion's Head were clear and in sharp relief against the blue of the sky. A gentle wind enhanced the aromatic scents of the mountain flora, and in the distance Jana could see the ocean was specked with white.

She would miss the beauty of the Peninsula, she

thought, as she slowed to let a squirrel scamper across the road unharmed. There was nothing in Johannesburg that could compare with it. And yet go back she must, and soon.

She tried to shake off the feeling of sadness which enveloped her. She should be glad to be going home. The Cape was beautiful; Devil's View was lovely beyond anything she had dreamed. But the loveliness was like that in a fairy-tale, for it could have no permanent relevance in her life. Johannesburg was many things. It was home, and it was Simon, and it was the place in which she and her husband would begin their new life together. It was right that she should be going back.

Briefly she thought of the innkeeper's warning. She was not concerned about the talk of people she had never met, but she could not help wondering why Miranda was circulating rumours. Jealousy? What did the voluptuous brunette have to be jealous about? Her position as future mistress of Devil's View seemed without question. If she was indeed jealous it could only be that she felt less secure than she had led Jana to believe. Although she did not like the girl, Jana could not help a brief moment of sympathy. It would not be easy to be the wife of Clint Dubois. He would be demanding and dictatorial. Could he also be tender? And for the woman who loved him, really loved him, and who was loved by him in return, would it not be a joy to yield to his uncompromising masculinity?

The question brought with it the customary stab of pain which she was beginning to associate with any thoughts of her employer.

As she drove up the mountain road she was filled with a sense of inevitability. Even before she had made the phone call she had known that the time had come for her to leave Devil's View. It was a knowledge which owed nothing to Miranda's jealousy, and very little to the fruitlessness of her search. The reason lay in Devil's View itself; in the house which she had grown to love as if it was indeed still her home. And, even more, the reason lay in its owner. She had not forgotten her rational-ising of a short while before. But she knew now that in her anger and hurt she had over-simplified the matter. It was true that she did not love Clint Dubois; it was not possible to love a man whose values, whose personality, were so totally alien from all she had hitherto cherished and held dear. But even if love did not enter into it—strange how often she had to convince herself of the fact—physical attraction certainly did. There was no denying his physical attraction, his allure—the sheer male sex-appeal of the man.

When he had insisted on her staying at Devil's View she had not had strong objections. True, she had been taken aback by the proposal, but she had felt the advantages of accepting his conditions out-weighed the problems.

What she had not expected was the way she her-self would become involved. In retrospect, she knew she had been foolish. Even on that first afternoon, when the waves had pushed her against Clint's hard male body, she had come alive under his touch, and since then her reactions had not dulled with familiarity. If anything they had grown stronger. He had only to come near her for her senses to reel in the most alarming way. Much as she knew she did not love him, there was nonetheless a real danger, if she did not put distance between them, that Clint Dubois would destroy her chance of happiness with Simon.

If her fiancé had not demanded that she return to Johannesburg, she would have had to persuade him that she could not continue with the quest; that she might never find the thing that she sought, if it even existed—a fact which she was beginning to doubt. Only to herself would she admit the truth. It was important that she make the break before the beautiful house and its masterful owner caught her so completely in the magic of their web that she would remain enmeshed in its skeins long after she had left the Cape.

Simon's insistence that she return had made things easier. At least she would not have his anger to contend with. All that now remained was to inform Clint of her intentions and to work her seven days of notice.

# CHAPTER SEVEN

Nobody was about when she came to Devil's View. She parked the Mini and slipped into the house through a side entrance. The papers on her desk were untouched. She sat down and began to work, typing quickly and competently; to her relief she had completed the correspondence before dark.

She hoped that Clint would not be in the dining-room when she came in for supper. Perhaps he and Miranda had decided to make a day of it, and had extended the afternoon to dinner in a restaurant on the foreshore. The less she saw of him in the little time that remained to her at Devil's View, the better. She would give him her notice early tomorrow morning.

When she came into the gracious room with its lovely stinkwood furniture, she saw that he was already at the table. The dark head lifted at her entrance. He did not speak, not even to say a polite good evening, but she saw that his eyes, almost black in the subdued lighting, studied her dispassionately. From his expression it was clear that he knew of her absence after lunch. She felt a deep blush rising to her cheeks. She was fuming silently as she bent to the soup which had been put before her. It was ridiculous that she should let him get to her like this. She was not a teenager to be castigated because she had left her post without permission; she was a mature young woman, with responsibility and discretion. Many was the time she had worked longer than necessary, and even today she had not covered her typewriter until the last letter was complete.

She would have liked to put her defence into words, but this was not possible when the accusations against her were not verbal but implied.

Dinner, as usual, was delicious. After a main course of delicately flavoured veal, there was a huge bowl of strawberries and whipped cream. But as with the lunch, Jana hardly tasted the food. They finished with coffee, and beneath lowered lashes she watched Clint drain his cup. She was still taking small sips from her own cup when he rose, murmured a few non-committal words and disappeared from the room. Was he off to spend the evening with Miranda, or did he intend to spend a few hours in his study working? For the first time it did not seem to matter. Even if Clint had left the house, Jana did not know if she would spend time searching. The urgency had gone from the quest, and her heart was no longer in it. With the knowledge that her days at Devil's View were numbered she was filled with a strange restlessness. It was as if she must drain every drop of beauty from the house and its surroundings, to store in her memory against the time when she would see it no more.

The dining-room had a door which opened on to

a small stoep at the side of the house. For a while she stood by the low stone wall and gazed out into the darkness. The night was cloudless and above the dark mass of the mountain the sky blazed with a million stars. The air was sweet with the scents of gardenias and wisteria and the countless mountain shrubs whose names Jana did not know. There was a peacefulness in the scene, a gentleness and a sense of rightness which brought a lump to her throat.

She left the stoep and wandered for a while through the garden. There were no street lights here, but the stars gave enough to see by. It was so quiet on the slope of the mountain, so utterly quiet that sounds which normally would be drowned by the noise of city traffic could be heard; the hum of the night insects, the croaking of a frog, the singing of the crickets. How she would miss it all when she left.

'You're not cold?' drawled a familiar voice.

She stopped quite still, her voice thumping painfully against her ribs. She had not noticed him in the darkness. A second or two, and her eyes were able to pick out the tall lean form standing against a low parapet.

'It's really quite mild,' she said, and wondered that her voice did not betray her shock.

'It is,' he agreed, and in the darkness his voice seemed even more vibrant than ever. 'Going far?'

Right out of your life, she thought. She could take the moment and give him her notice. But no, she would do that in the clear light of morning when emotion would not rear its head.

'Just for a walk,' she said lightly. 'It's such a beautiful evening.'

'It is.' His tone was so mild that she was not prepared for the question when he sprang it. 'You played truant this afternoon. Where did you go?'

She should not have been surprised. She had known when she came in for supper that he was aware of her absence. Nevertheless, she could not prevent the tension which threatened to make a hard knot in her stomach.

'My work is all finished,' she said defensively, when she had herself in control.

'That wasn't the question. Where were you?' There was authority in the quiet voice, the authority of a man who was not accustomed to being left without an answer.

She tried to sustain the defiance, but it did not seem possible. 'I ... I had to go somewhere.' It came out shakily.

'Where?'

It should have been so easy to tell him the truth. What kept her back? Fear of what he would say when he discovered that she had lied to him right from the start? Or the fact that she could not bear his contempt? For to Clint the whole purpose of the search would appear ridiculous.

'.... Somewhere.'

In a single lithe movement the lean figure had detached itself from the shadows. She felt a strong

hand on her shoulder as he spun her round to face
him. 'There must be a reason why you're so secretive.'

She shook her head numbly.

'A man?' The grip on her shoulder tightened
a fraction. 'You go to meet somebody?'

'No.' The word slipped out hoarsely. She tried
to escape from his grip, but, as before, she found
that his strength was greater than hers. 'Of course
not!'

He laughed, the sound soft and husky in the dark
stillness, and with a quality that was so seductive
that it sent a flicker through her nerve-stream.

'No "of course not" about it,' he observed, and
his voice was as seductive as his laugh. 'I told you
once before that you were a desirable female.'

'As desirable as Miranda?' The question had
slipped out entirely without volition. What was this
crazy madness that had taken hold of her, so that
she could no longer control even her words? She
would have given anything to take back the question, yet overriding her embarrassment was the
need for an answer.

'The eternal female,' he mocked her. 'Mirror,
mirror on the wall....'

'Well?' she threw at him. Having gone thus far,
she could not resist the temptation to go further.

'Who is the most desirable of them all?' A sardonic parody. The hand descended from her
shoulder, lean fingers trailing to the smooth vulnerable portion on her inner arm, down to her wrist,

and tips of his fingers moving so provocatively that Jana felt a fire that was more like a pain shooting through her body.

'What a test of your desirability?'

She opened her mouth to protest, but the quick pressure of his lips prevented all speech. There was neither passion nor tenderness in his kisses. Just a tantalising expertise which ignited inside her an agonising delight. His hands moved downwards to her hips, moulding her to him, and instinctively her body arched to his.

He put her from him quite abruptly. The movement was perhaps the most shocking she had ever experienced, and she stared at him through a blur, disappointed and bereft. He had taken a pipe from his pocket, and was proceeding to light it with a coolness which indicated that what had just happened between them had not moved him in the slightest.

'Well?' came the cool mocking tones. 'Have I proved any point?'

Her heart was still hammering from the assault on her senses, and now she was angry. How dared he make fun of her like this! What hurt most was the fact that while she had been half delirious from the embrace, Clint himself had felt nothing.

'Rotten swine!' she hissed at him.

'Not at all, my dear,' was the caustic rejoinder. 'I only gave you what you asked for.'

She opened her mouth, only to close it again. There was no sense in hurling at him all the insults and accusations that came to mind. He would dismiss them all with an infuriating coldness and finality. She would be the loser in any encounter with this man. Better to retrieve the shreds of her dignity and remain silent.

She lifted her shoulders and stood very straight, chin tilted high. She would say a frigid goodnight and leave him out here in the velvet darkness. And in the morning she would hand him her notice.

Something of her thoughts must have shown in her bearing. She was turning away from him when she heard the low chuckle. 'We are not amused?' he teased her.

'No.' With icy dignity.

'Perhaps you'll acquire a little more subtlety when you grow up.' Another nerve-tingling laugh as a hand shot out, gripping her wrist and stopping her from leaving. 'Before you start hurling insults, let me remind you that you are my employee.'

'But not your slave,' she flung at him. 'Let me go!'

'Not before we've had a talk.'

'I don't have to tell you where I went,' she attacked breathlessly.

A lifted eyebrow intimated that if he insisted on knowing, he could force her to tell him. But his question was: 'Have you read the book on Louis Thibault?'

The architect who had designed Devil's View.... Her eyes flickered upwards at the question that seemed to have no bearing on anything that had been said. She remembered now seeing the book in her office. Clint must have put it there for her to read. In self-defence she was moved to tell a lie. '.... Yes.'

'You found it interesting?' The quiet drawl tantalised and infuriated.

'Extremely.' Her voice was cool.

'Strange that you managed to leave the tiny piece of paper on top of the book undisturbed.' He spoke quietly, conversationally. It took a moment for the impact of his words to sink in. When it did, she felt the treacherous warmth flood her cheeks.

'You've been spying on me,' she said shakily.

'Just checking,' came the dry rejoinder.

She was quiet for a moment, trying to gather the thoughts that rushed chaotically through her mind. 'What of it?' she asked at length, as calmly as she could.

'Your interest in Cape Dutch architecture is not quite as deep as you try to make me believe.'

'I don't rely on books,' she informed him loftily. 'I prefer the evidence of my eyes.' She hesitated, thinking madly as she improvised. 'I like to absorb atmosphere ... character....'

She stopped, gulping as his thumb began a sensual exploration of the inside of her wrist. 'Do you have to do that?'

'No.' But the movement did not stop. 'Jana, I want to talk to you.'

'All right. But ... but leave go my hand!'

'If that's what you want.' He dropped his hand

abruptly, and she knew it wasn't what she had wanted at all. Stiffly, with all her dignity, she waited for him to speak.

'I still don't know your reasons for being at Devil's View.' His tone was cool, dispassionate. 'But we both know it isn't your interest in architecture that keeps you here. No!'—his hand shot out as she was about to protest—'I'm not interested in your explanations. I just want to know one thing. Do you intend to stay on?'

Her limbs froze. She looked at him as if mesmerised. His face was a chiselled mask, grim and rugged and devastatingly attractive. She could not read his eyes, but she saw the strong line of the jaw, the tautness of his lips. Now was the moment to say what she had to. True, she had intended delaying her notice till morning, but circumstances had changed. She was being given the opportunity to talk now.

'Why must you know?' she whispered.

'I'm embarking on a project—a big project.' Behind the dispassionate control she could detect a tautness which caught at her heart.

'What kind of project?'

'For some time now I've been doing research into a disease which attacks the young vines. It's a disease that's the scourge of the vineyards. I think I've made a breakthrough.'

He had not moved away, but nevertheless he was apart from her now. He was so tall, she thought, looking up at him from beneath her lashes, so strong and sure and virile, so compellingly male. He could make her senses reel just by his nearness. He knew his power over women, and enjoyed it. But he was more than just a playboy. With rapt attention she listened as he talked about the vineyards, about the disease that could attack swiftly and silently, before the grapes were ripe, preventing a full harvest.

Now he was wholly a farmer, dedicated, sincere, interested in the grapes that were his living and his life. Interested in research not only for the good of Devil's View but for the good of every wine farmer in the Cape. Jana felt a lump grow at the back of her throat.

After a while he stopped talking and stood staring into the darkness. He did not look at Jana. It was as if he had forgotten she existed. There was strength in the autocratic figure, and pride, and also a great loneliness. Jana had to quell a desire to reach out and touch him.

'Where do I come in?' she asked at last, very quietly.

He turned, and she saw that his eyes were hooded, his face a little bleak. 'I want you to type the project,' he told her.

'Will it take long?' More than a week? Because that's all the time I have.

'A month or two.' He must have heard her gasp, because he glanced down at her curiously. 'It's not as formidable as it sounds. I won't expect more of you than you can manage.'

'What ... what makes you think I can do it?' she asked a little breathlessly.

'I don't think—I know.' There was certainty in his tone. 'You're very competent.'

'Thank you,' she said miserably, because she didn't know what else to say.

She was aware that he was studying her, and knew that he could detect the hopelessness in her face, the droop of her shoulders. She was glad that it was too dark for him to see the pallor in her cheeks and the tears that trembled on her lashes.

'Will you stay?' Again the tautness.

Tell him, urged her mind. Take the moment and tell him you're going. But it was her heart which seemed to have the upper hand, and it was her heart which stopped her from doing what she knew to be right.

'I'm here,' she prevaricated.

'Don't play games with me, Jana.' There was steel in the hand that gripped her chin, forcing her head backwards, so that she had to look into his eyes. 'This is something I must know.'

'Why?'

'Because,' he said slowly, 'if you take on the work, you must be prepared to remain here until it's complete. Once you've begun, you have to go on. That's the way it is, Jana.'

'It's so important to you?' Vainly she searched the dark eyes for any sign of expression.

'Yes.' She saw that a muscle had tightened.

She had not intended to ask the question, except

that it was one she had often pondered. 'Why did all your other secretaries leave?'

His eyes narrowed, and she saw the thinning of the lips. 'I sent them packing.' His voice was cool, crisp, matter-of-fact. He studied her for a moment, and she saw his mouth curve in a sardonic grin. 'Disappointed?'

She shook her head. She wished she could control the beating of her heart. 'But why?'

'Because they didn't meet my standards.'

As secretaries or as women? Could she ask him? For some reason it seemed terribly important that she should know. Another quick glance at the handsome face, chiselled and strong in the darkness. She saw the arrogance and the power and the latent ruthlessness. She saw the well-shaped lips, and remembered his reaction after her provocative question. She kept her own lips pressed tightly together.

'Well, Jana, will you stay?'

A shudder went through the slim body. Tomorrow she would curse herself for being foolish and irrational. But this was tonight, and the lean hard body of Clint Dubois was so close to her that she could feel his warmth through the thin fabric of her clothes. As she gave him her decision she knew that nothing could ever be quite the same for her again. Very softly she said, 'I'll stay, Mr Dubois.'

'Clint,' he told her. 'From now on you'll call me Clint.'

She had no time to ponder the implications of this new development, for his mouth descended again, his lips finding hers with unerring sureness. He had never kissed her like this before. It was a gentle kiss, brief yet tender. A kiss to seal a bargain, she thought despairingly, nothing more.

She was shivering when he released her. 'You're cold,' he said softly. 'Go inside now, Jana. I'll see you in the morning.'

Simon was furious: she could almost feel the outrage which quivered through the wires. He demanded that she give in her notice as she had promised, and that she catch the next plane back to Johannesburg. He swore and threatened, and when that failed he cajoled. But Jana remained adamant: she would stay at Devil's View until the project was finished. When he slammed down the phone he did not tell her first that he loved her, and this time she did not ask.

Later she sat in the shade of a chestnut tree, and relived what had happened. The call with Simon had left her shaken. He was hurt and angry, and she was the cause of it. There had been a time when his pleadings would have had her flying back to Johannesburg on the first available plane, so happy that he wanted her with him, that nothing else mattered.

But things had changed. Not basic things, perhaps. She still loved Simon, *of course* she loved Simon. And she meant to marry him. But the last few days had shown her that she was not just a mindless girl of twenty-four, engaged to be married and eager to please her fiancé to the extent that she had agreed to undertake a thousand-mile trip for a reason which she resented. She was also Jana Harvey. She was intelligent and eager and had a mind of her own. She was enthusiastic about the project outlined by her employer, and determined to work with him. In his fury, Simon had accused her of being a Women's Libber, and Jana had resisted the temptation to tell him that he was a chauvinist male. Nothing would have been achieved. Insults and counter-insults could not improve their relationship. The thought came into her mind, if Simon was a male chauvinist, what did that make Clint Dubois? For sheer arrogance and self-confidence she had yet to meet her employer's match. And yet there was a difference....

In the moments before she had fallen asleep last night she had thought that perhaps the light of morning would make her see the folly of agreeing to stay on at Devil's View. She did see it—but she would not go back on her word. Dimly she realised that there might be sadness at the end of it all, inevitable sorrow when the time came to leave Devil's View—and Clint.

Her one consolation was that when she left here, Simon would be waiting. She would be so busy with preparations for her wedding that any sadness at leaving Devil's View would be drowned in all the excitement.

Simon.... She tried to shake off the feeling of depression which had been with her since the phone-call. It was natural that he was angry, but she hoped that when he had got over his rage he would understand that it was important for her to do one worthwhile thing quite on her own before she was married. Perhaps then he would comprehend that she was a person in her own right, and he would respect her for it.

Simon.... There was so much that distressed her. When she spoke to him on the phone there was just his voice, that curiously disembodied voice talking to her from a thousand miles away. Why didn't his image come with it? And why did she find herself thinking of him less and less often? Was it because another man's face was intruding itself ever more strongly, not only in her mind, but in her emotions, her senses?

No! Violently she shied away from the thought, like a nervous young horse. But the thought came back, persisted.

Useless to deny the elation that filled her at the knowledge that she was remaining a while longer at Devil's View. Or to deny the exultation at the thought of working with Clint on a project that was important and innovative, and which would benefit not only the vineyards of Devil's View, but those of thousands of other farmers.

But until now she had not realised how displaced her priorities had become, so that working with Clint was more important than her future with Simon. With every nerve and fibre she was looking forward to the weeks that lay ahead. She would not change her mind about staying on at Devil's View even if because of it Simon decided against their marriage. And that thought was perhaps the most disturbing of all.

Jana had risen early, so that she could make the telephone call before the day's work began. The dining-room had been empty when she had gone in for breakfast—nothing unusual in that, for it was very seldom that she and Clint had the meal together. It was not until she sat in her office that she saw him for the first time since their talk.

When the door opened and he came into the room, all her rationalising did not stop the wild leaping of her senses. He must have been riding, for he wore well-cut corded breeches which emphasised the muscularity of the long legs. A blue-grey high-necked sweater deepened the colour of his eyes. The skin of his face glowed, as if it had been buffeted by the wind. He looked fresh and healthy, and as he stepped near her she experienced an irrational desire to reach out and touch him. She dropped her eyes, fearful that he would read the emotions sweeping through her.

'Good morning, Jana.' His tone was cool and crisp, like his appearance.

'Good morning.' She hesitated a moment. It was not easy to form the name aloud for the first time, even though she had said it dozens of times in her mind. 'Clint.'

'Ready for work?' Something in his tone made her look up. He was smiling, a rare smile which brought warmth to his eyes. It was a smile which made him look human, as he so seldom did. He knew how difficult it had been for her to say his name, but he did not mind.

'Yes, I'm ready.' She could no more stem the eagerness in her tone than she could prevent the colour from rushing to her cheeks. 'I'm so excited about the project, Clint.' There, she had said it again, and this time it was easier.

'I'm glad.' That spark of warmth again. 'But we won't begin in earnest till Monday.'

'Oh?' Disappointment clouded great emerald eyes. 'I thought....'

'I have a few letters for you, and I want you to do them as quickly as you can. No flitting off in your Mini.' A wicked flash of white teeth, and a low chuckle at her instant discomfiture. 'When you've finished, I want you to go to your room and pack a few things.'

'Pack?' She stared at him uncomprehendingly.

'Did you know I have a little fishing cottage near Hermanus?' And as she shook her head: 'I'm tired. I need a few days' break before we get down to the nitty-gritty of the project.'

'You ... you said I should pack....' Her words were fumbling, as were the thoughts in her mind. 'You don't mean....'

'You'll be coming with me, of course.' Spoken

with matter-of-factness, as if he saw nothing untoward in the idea.

'Just ... just you and me?' she asked, a little breathlessly.

Grey eyes gazed down into green ones, and the warmth which had been there for such a short while was replaced by a familiar mockery. 'Well, well,' he drawled. 'Sudden scruples?'

'Not sudden,' Jana defended herself.

'You live with me at Devil's View; you'll be with me in the fishing cottage. Where's the difference?'

'Devil's View is big, and there are the servants...' Her words trailed away. She was confused. A few minutes ago she had been in the grip of an unfamiliar happiness. Now with every word she was reducing herself to the stature of a small and foolish girl.

An eyebrow lifted, and she had to look away from the sardonic amusement which curved the corners of his mouth. 'So you've felt yourself chaperoned here at Devil's View? Even though the servants don't sleep in the house?'

There were times when she felt too miserable to counter his sarcasm with her own. Numbly she shook her head. 'Do you have a servant at the cottage?'

'I do not. Which means you'll cook and keep house along with your other duties.' The low chuckle which could send the adrenalin pumping through her veins. 'Perhaps if I tell you that there are two rooms in the cottage you won't mind so much. Well, little Jana?'

The use of the word 'little' was deliberate. It was to show her that he thought of her as young and very innocent. Curiously it did not hurt as much as it could have. Little Jana. . . . The words almost had the sound of a caress.

'Still have any qualms?'

'Yes,' she answered him, and this time her eyes sparkled with a glimmer of mischief. 'But with a wall between us I'm ready to take the risk.' She hesitated. 'Clint, if all you want is a break, why do you want me to come with you?'

'It might not be a complete break. I want to turn over some ideas, a few loose ends that my tidy mind can't quite accept. And I want you to be there so that you can take notes if need be.'

The words squashed completely any thoughts that he wanted her with him because he enjoyed her company. And still she could not quell the excitement which came from knowing that for two days she would be quite alone with Clint in a small cottage far from Cape Town.

The excitement persisted as she typed the few letters he wanted, then went upstairs to her room to pack. Just the necessities, he had said. She packed quickly—toiletries and some underwear, a change of jeans and a crisp scarlet shirt, a cardigan. At the last moment she added her bikini. The cottage was near the sea, and it was likely that they would

spend time on the beach, she told herself, as if
the matter needed justifying. Which was absurd.
The bikini was as much a necessity as everything
else. But as she closed her suitcase she could not
help wondering if Clint would recognise the garment and remember the circumstances in which
she had worn it once before.

# CHAPTER EIGHT

THE sun was high as they left Cape Town and its
environs far behind them. This was the beginning
of the Garden Route Jana knew, the famous scenic
drive leading from the mother city eastwards to
Port Elizabeth. They were going only as far as
Hermanus, but as she thrilled to the beauty all
around her Jana vowed that some day she would
travel all the way.

Sitting forward in her seat, she thought that
never in her life had she seen so much beauty.
Johannesburg and the Highveld had a grandeur of
their own, but for sheer scenic loveliness she thought
the Cape Peninsula must be unsurpassed. There
was the sea on one side, a vivid Prussian blue, with
the sunshine making a crystal pathway on the water.
On the other side stood the mountains, brooding,
majestic. There were glimpses of beaches, wide and
golden, and bridges and lagoons. There were forests
and wild flowers and once a herd of wind-blown
antelope. And there were mountain passes, high
and awesome and with incredible views.

Clint was silent, almost as if he knew that Jana
had never travelled this road. It came to her quite
suddenly that there was no reason why he should
think her a stranger to the Cape. She had never told

him her home was in Johannesburg....

She turned slightly in her seat and stole a glance at him, hoping that she was unobserved. His eyes were on the road, and he did not turn his head at her gaze. Even in profile there was something ruggedly attractive about him. A line ran from nose to mouth, furrowing his face in a manner that was intensely masculine—a laughter line, she thought, and wondered why she had never noticed it before. Perhaps because she had so rarely seen him laugh? His window was open, and his dark hair was ruffled in the breeze. He sat easily in the seat, his hands, long-fingered and tanned, holding the wheel with the same confident expertise which was evident in everything he did. They were on a winding section of road now, and she could see that his whole attention was on driving, but there was no tension, no nervousness, as he negotiated the steep bends. With a lesser driver Jana might have had her fearful moments, but not with Clint. It occurred to her that she could trust Clint Dubois with her life.

With an effort she tore her gaze from the compelling profile, and back to the passing countryside. Sir Lowrey's Pass, Somerset West, the Strand— names she had read of and heard spoken took substance bneath her eyes. They stopped once at an inn for some coffee. It had been a coaching inn once, long before the days of motorised transport. They talked very little as they sat on the sunny stoep, with its vista of blue sea and pounding surf. When they had finished their coffee they went back to the car and did not stop again until they reached Hermanus.

They drove right through the little seaside resort and carried on along the main road another few miles. Then Clint turned on to a sand road. The track was winding and bumpy and so isolated that Jana marvelled that there could be a habitable dwelling at the end of it. Another twist in the road, and when Clint stopped the car there was a little gasp of delight from Jana. Nestling in the folds of the mountain, and surrounded on all sides by trees, the cottage was like the fishermen's home in a fairy-tale. It was small, and had once been white, but the paint had long since peeled off, resulting in an indeterminate colour which blended comfortably with the setting. Ivy grew over the walls, and in the pretence of a garden were small clumps of sea-roses. A far cry from Devil's View. Stealing a quick glance at the man who owned both places, Jana wondered whether the few days in isolation would reveal a new aspect of a person who was even more complex than she had imagined.

It was only when she got out of the car that she realised quite how small the cottage was, and she forgot the picturesque aspect of the place as a new thought struck her. Staring at the cottage, she was unaware that her small oval face betrayed her thoughts very clearly to a perceptive spectator.

She spun round at the sound of the low chuckle, and saw his wicked grin of delight. 'Scared?'

'N—no,' she denied uncertainly.

'Liar! You're wondering about the sleeping accommodation.'

There was little point in denying it. 'How did you guess?'

The corners of his mouth lifted further. 'I'm beginning to know you very well, Jana Harvey.' A hand encircled her throat, just the pressure of his thumb beneath her chin enough to make her look up at him. 'Don't you know that?'

Tongues of flame flickered from her neck down her spinal cord, and beneath his fingers the pulse at the base of her throat was throbbing like a small caged bird. There was something in his eyes which she had never seen before and could not quite define. It was becoming impossible to meet his gaze. Her head and her throat might be captive, but she was still able to conceal her eyes beneath her long-lashed lids.

'Please....' There was a tiny sob in her voice as she tried to pull away from him. He let her go very easily, almost as if she had answered the question to his satisfaction. But she hadn't answered, not directly. Or had she....? Her senses were reeling, so that it was hard to think.

Clint went to the back of the car and opened the boot to bring out the suitcases. Jana bent toward a clump of sea-roses, pretending to examine them, while in reality she was striving for composure. Had she been mad to come with him? she wondered. Was there a way in which she could have got out of the trip? He had been so very definite.... Besides, if she had argued and refused to accompany him, with whom would she have fought the harder battle, with Clint or with herself? Again the flash of revelation and with it the self-knowledge that was becoming more and more difficult to deny.

She straightened as a long shadow formed beside her. 'Brave girl,' he murmured beside her ear, and there was something other than irony in his tone. 'There really are two rooms.'

He opened the door and stood aside to let her go in. It took just a moment to see that he had been telling the truth. The sight of two doors was so reassuring that she was able to study the interior of the cottage with something akin to pleasure. It was dim and cool and the air was a little musty, but not unpleasantly so. What struck her most forcibly was the charm of the cottage. It was simple, but not in a studied way, not as if its wealthy owner had set out to make it deliberately rustic. The long cane chairs, the kerosene lamps, the stack of fishing-gear and the small bookcase with its pile of old novels, all had their natural place here.

'Well?'

She turned, caught by an unaccustomed eagerness in his tone. Was it possible that even Clint Dubois was human enough to need occasional approval? 'It's lovely,' she told him warmly.

'I'm glad you like it,' he said, as if he meant it. Incredibly, it seemed that her opinion had mattered to him. Her heart leaped.

'Tired?' he was asking.

'Oh, no!'

'How about making some tea? You'll find everything there.' A nod towards a gas cooker and a small shelf of crockery and staple groceries in one corner. 'Afterwards we'll go for a swim.'

She watched him light the cooker, and then she filled the kettle, and set out cups and saucers and opened a packet of biscuits, and all the while she was filled with a strange and restless joy. Nearly three days stretched before her, three days alone with Clint in this cottage far from Devil's View. She had to remind herself that Clint had brought her with him only because she was his secretary; that even on holiday he could never be altogether relaxed. But the reminder did not dim the happiness which brought an upward tilt to her lips, and a sparkle to her eyes.

They drank their tea on a tiny stoep overlooking the sea, and afterwards they changed into their swim-wear. Clint had told her which room would be hers. It was the smaller of the two rooms, also the more private. Like the rest of the cottage it was simple, furnished with only the bare necessities, and yet with a charm of its own. As she closed the door her eyes went to the lock. She was uncertain whether to use it, but it was reassuring to know it was there if she needed it.

On one wall was a mirror. When she had changed into her bikini Jana studied her appearance with a sense of misgiving. The bikini seemed to have shrunk since the last time she had worn it, or was it just her heightened awareness which noted the way the tiny garment revealed the curves of firm breasts and sleekly rounded hips?

She had never been conscious of her figure. She loved to swim and to sunbathe, and the hours spent beside the pool at the house of Simon's parents had been relaxed and undemanding. Today, for the first time, the idea of appearing in her bikini made her shy. Would Clint find her figure wanting? It had become disturbingly important that he should approve.

If she could have changed her mind about swimming, she would have. But with Clint's perceptiveness he would know the reason, and his mockery would be deadly. Slipping a towelling wrap around her shoulders, she lifted her chin and opened the door.

He stood beside the window, examining a fishing-rod. At sight of him excitement snatched at her heart. But for the day she had met him on the beach at Fish Hoek, she had never seen Clint in anything but shirts and trousers. Now he had on swimming-trunks. His feet were bare and his long legs were bronzed, and above the band of the trunks she could see his chest, also bronzed, and covered with dark hair. She remembered being held against the bare chest on that first afternoon, before she had known that he was the owner of Devil's View, and with the memory came an odd shortness of breath.

Sensing her presence, he looked up from the rod.

His eyes lingered on her a moment, and for no reason at all she felt colour warm her face. Then he smiled and stretched out a hand.

'That was quick. Most females seem to take an hour to change. Let's go, Jana.'

Most females. . . . Along with the happiness which had been with her since leaving Cape Town, there was a small twinge of pain. Which other females had he brought to this cottage hidden amongst the trees? Miranda?

She could not continue to brood as they took the path that led to the beach. Evidently it was used only rarely, for the path was an overgrown riot of scrub and sea-bushes. Roots were a tangle underfoot, and beach-sand sifted through bare toes. At one point the undergrowth was so dense that Clint forced up a bough while Jana crawled underneath. Then he took her hand and helped her the rest of the way.

He was still holding her hand when they emerged on to the beach, and Jana let him keep it. At a clump of rocks they threw down their towels.

'You can take off the wrap.' The familiar drawl held a hint of amusement.

Beneath the knowing scrutiny in the dark eyes, her shyness increased. 'I . . . might get burned,' she prevaricated.

'By the sun?' The suggestion was slyly provocative.

'Clint. . . .'

'If you won't take it off, then I must.' His hands

went so quickly to her shoulders that she was unprepared. In one swift movement he had drawn off the wrap. Jana felt very young, very vulnerable, as she stood before him in the brief green bikini, and watched his eyes taking in every inch of her body. His gaze rested a few moments on the small oval face, noting the flushed cheeks and the heightened colour in the large emerald eyes. Unhurriedly the gaze dropped, lingering on the pulse beating wildly at the base of the throat, on the rise and fall of softly rounded breasts; then travelled further to the smooth midriff and the slim bare legs.

When he looked up again his eyes were speculative. She looked at him questioningly, not daring to speak.

'Nice.' He was smiling. 'Even nicer than I'd remembered.'

'Thank you.' She was a little breathless.

'But a little pale. Not as tanned as I expect of a girl who spends her free time on the beach.'

He was still smiling, but the laziness in his tone was belied by a thoughtful expression. Jana was instantly on her guard.

'I've had very little free time these last weeks,' she reminded him. Don't question me now, she pleaded silently. Don't spoil this short time we have together.

He looked at her a moment longer, grey eyes steady as they gazed into green ones. But the accusation she feared did not come. Instead he said lightly, 'Do you have sun-tanning oil?'

She shook her head, and watched him take a small bottle from his shirt pocket. She took it from him and rapidly spread oil on her legs and her tummy and then her neck and shoulders. She was closing the bottle when Clint took it from her.

'Turn your back,' he ordered.

'I ... I don't think....' She swallowed nervously.

'For heaven's sake, woman! Don't go coy on me. Do you think I want a sun-blistered secretary?'

Nothing for it. She kept her eyes down as she turned. As she waited for the feel of his hand on her back she braced instinctively.

'Marie Antoinette braving herself for the guillotine.' She was glad that he could not see her face as a long finger drew seductively across the back of her neck. Damn the man, could he read every one of her thoughts? If so, then he would also know.... She shook her head violently, as if by so doing she could throw out an entirely new thought.

The haunting laugh came from so near that she thought he must hear every beat of her hammering heart. 'A strong denial.' There was a hint of mockery in his tone. 'You must be more frightened than I realised.'

She was frightened, yes, but not of what he might do. The thing she feared was inside her. It was a danger from which there might be no more escape.

As his hands touched her back and began to rub in the oil it took an almost superhuman effort for Jana to maintain an outward appearance of calm. The slow rhythmic movements were unbearably sensuous. He was tantalising her with his fingers, stirring her senses till she felt she must break away from him or lose her mind.

'Let's swim,' she suggested, and wondered if he heard the raggedness in her voice.

She was glad that Clint did not take her hand as they ran to the water. In one way or another the physical contact of the last few minutes had been more shattering than anything she had experienced.

The feel of cold water splashing about her hips was both a shock and a relief. She dived into a wave, then stood up, shaking the wet hair from her face.

'Coming in further?' A statue fired in copper and bronze, she thought, looking at the muscled torso. He was so close to her that she could see every one of the black hairs that clung to the broad chest.

'I wouldn't like to hit a whirlpool.' She tossed the joke off as lightly as she was able.

'Very sensible.' The seductive voice mocked her. 'I might not rescue you in time, and I wouldn't like to lose a competent worker.'

'Clint Dubois!' she threw at him. 'You are the most....'

'Infuriating man you ever met,' he finished for her. 'Don't go out of your depth, Jana.' And with that he swam away.

Just a short while ago she might have been tempted to swim after him, to prove to him that she could swim as well as he did. But then there had been no desire to prove anything else.

A wave lifted her, and she drifted unresistingly with the swell. Clint was swimming. She could see his dark head, and the arms that cleaved the water with a stroke that was deceptively easy.

He had been joking, of course, when he had made the remark about not wanting to lose a competent secretary. But basically the joke had been no more than the truth. If Clint thought of her at all it was only as an employee, a girl who could spell accurately, who could keep his correspondence up to date, and who could be entrusted with the important task of helping him with his project.

Which was as it should be. She had applied for a job. She should be glad that she came up to his rigid standards when all her predecessors had failed. Besides, she was engaged to be married to another man; her interest in Devil's View should lie solely in the house and the secret somewhere within its walls. It was absurd, this wish which was becoming more important than anything else—that Clint should think of her as a woman.

The tide was low and the sea was calm. Turning on to her back, Jana lifted her feet from the sandy floor and let herself float. The sky was a deep blue, with just a few small clouds breaking its vastness. The beach was deserted. It seemed that the main bathing beach was some distance away, but Clint had assured her that it was safe to swim here. There was no reason to dispute the fact. Instinctively she knew that Clint would not take chances with a person's life.

Beyond the shore rose mountains and forests, and near the water-line a flock of gulls screamed and fought. It was all so beautiful, Jana thought, and tried to concentrate on the view. Which was hard.... Much as she tried to push them away, her thoughts kept returning to the moments on the beach when Clint had rubbed the suntan oil into her back. As if his fingers were touching her now, she could feel the stroking movements, evocative and sensuous. Restlessly her hands splashed up some water. The act had meant nothing to him—at least nothing more than that he had wanted to spare her the agony of a bad sunburn. Perhaps, she thought wryly, he had actually been thinking only of himself. On Monday it would be back to work, and if Jana was badly burned she might not be able to give of her best.

Why had those moments meant quite so much? she wondered. So, Clint had sex-appeal: she knew that already. But Simon was sexy too. He *must* be. He was good-looking and attractive, and she had always enjoyed his kisses.

She could remember Simon oiling her back, many times. Despairingly she cast her mind to the Sundays beside the pool.... Why was it that Simon had never stirred her in quite the same way?

Perhaps after all she had been foolish to allow Clint to persuade her to remain at Devil's View until the project was complete. Even more foolish to accompany him on this week-end. Foolish? Crazy was more like it. Utterly crazy not to realise that the spell which had been born at Devil's View might grow even stronger in this isolated place beside the sea. So strong that her chances of breaking free were becoming ever more remote. When more and more of her waking moments were concerned with Clint, how much hope was there that she would forget him when she drove through the tall iron gates of Devil's View for the last time?

Somehow she must retrieve her sanity. Her only hope was to keep her distance from Clint—not an easy matter when the very nature of their accommodation forced them into a greater proximity than they had known until now. Somehow she must do it. She would be remote, cool, detached, the competent secretary who had accompanied her employer only because of a complete dedication to her work. He had said he wanted to sort out his ideas, tie up loose ends. She would carry a notebook with her wherever they went, and let him dare to make fun of her. She would. . . .

What further precautions she would take were pushed from her mind as two hands seized her from behind. 'By God, if it isn't a mermaid!' observed a laughing voice.

She stared up at him, her eyes wide. No man had the right to look so devastatingly handsome. Eyes, clear and grey beneath long black lashes and well-defined brows. Teeth strong and even and very white against the deep tan. Jawline firm and well-shaped. A bronze and well-muscled torso. Sea-gods, with all their primitive magnetism, should remain at the bottom of the sea. They had no place in real life, where any struggle to fight them was so unfairly weighted that it was lost before it had ever begun.

But fight she must. For a few moments she had continued to float passively, while his hands kept their hold on her waist. Now she dropped her feet and tried to stand, but he was too quick for her. His hands slid beneath her hips and without any effort he pulled her weightless body to him, resting it against his thighs. Then he bent and kissed her. His lips were cool and firm, and when her own lips parted, there was the taste of sea and salt. One hand remained beneath her hips, the other hand moved over her body, sensuously, possessively, staking an impossible claim. She held on to that thought for a brief moment, as her body yearned to be even closer to his.

His kisses changed, growing harder, more insistent, moving from an exploration of her mouth to her eyes, her ears, descending to the hollow at the base of her throat. As his lips moved even lower, finding the roundness of breasts where the bikini ended, it was no longer possible to hold on to rational thought. Now there was only the world of the senses. The feel of taut thighs and a heartbeat that was rhythmic and strong. The taste of lips that moved as if with a mind of their own.

Without thinking she leaned up and twined her arms about his neck. No questioning, no reasoning. What her mind said did not seem to matter; her body told her she belonged to this man.

She heard his swift intake of breath, and then he lifted his head. She opened her eyes. His arms were still holding her to him, but the sun was in her eyes so that she could not see his expression. She had not thought it possible for her heart to beat still faster, but it did.

'Sea-witch,' he murmured, and she heard the roughness in his voice.

He began to draw her to him once more, then pulled away with an abruptness which left her feeling disappointed and bereft. 'Wait for me on the beach,' he ordered, and there was something in his voice which she did not understand.

Jana towelled herself dry, then lay down and closed her eyes. Why had he put her from him when he did? She had been so stirred that she was ready to do anything that he asked. Did he know it? He could hardly be unaware of her ardour. Had he been saving her from herself? A strange thought indeed.

The notebook was to have been her saviour—a wry smile at the memory. Notebook and pencil had had no place in the scheme of things. In those moments with Clint there had been only the vastness of the sky and the pounding of the surf and the hard long body of the man who, despite all her rationalising, was beginning to mean more than life itself.

She did not think of the notebook again that day; not when she and Clint walked along a seem-

ingly endless beach, with the golden sand warm
beneath their toes, and the incoming waves curling
around their ankles; not when they climbed a high
cliff-path and watched the breakers hurl themselves
on to the rocks below; not in the late afternoon
when Jana sat on a rock, hollowed into a seat by
wind and waves, and watched as Clint fished for
their supper.

He stood at a point some distance away. He had
forbidden her to accompany him there, saying it
was too dangerous. Fearless and sure, he stood, with
his legs braced and slightly apart to withstand the
onslaught of the waves. At Devil's View he was
every inch the master of the great wine estate. Here,
in T-shirt and faded jeans rolled up to his knees,
he seemed at one with the sea and the sky and the
elements. Jana watched as he threw his line, grace
and power in every curve of arm and rod, and her
heart went out to the lonely figure on the rocky
promontory.

When he joined her he was carrying three fish—
turbot, he told her. They would not starve.

'You don't expect me to clean them?' she asked
in pretended horror.

'Sure.' Again the rare warmth in his smile. 'Any
woman worth her salt can gut a fish.'

'Count this one out!'

'A bargain. I'll clean, you'll cook. Agreed?'

'Agreed.'

They walked back along the beach in the fading
light of the day, and there was joy in their to-

getherness, in the feeling of being close beside each other, though never touching. Joy in the absence of mockery and derision.

It grew dark, and there was joy in the meal they shared beneath the stars. Clint cleaned the fish with a skill which astonished Jana. He had made a fire beneath a metal grid, and when she had seasoned the fish they let it grill over the dying flames. The fish was tasty and tender. They ate it with a simple salad and a bottle of white wine from the cellars of Devil's View. Jana could not remember when she had enjoyed a meal so much.

Long after they had finished their meal, and the last embers had faded to nothing, Clint and Jana still sat outside. The air was warm and fragrant, and even above the ceaseless roar of the surf there was the song of the night insects. Silence had fallen between the two people outside the little cottage. A companionable silence which seemed to transcend the need for conversation. There was a sense of rightness about it all, Jana thought, and with it came an inkling of how it would be to be married to Clint. There was sadness in the thought, and she tried to push it away. Marriage was the one thing that could never happen between them. But memory would stay with her always. This was one evening that she knew she would remember all her life.

She wondered if he would touch her when they rose to go to bed. Part of her wanted him to, wanted it desperately. The other part knew it was wiser

if he did not, because she would not have the
strength or the desire to resist his lovemaking. But
she need not have worried. Inside the cottage he
gave her a lighted kerosene lamp to take with her
to her room. 'Sleep well, little one,' he said, and the
softness of his tone made the words a caress.

She lay awake a long time. She heard Clint moving about the other room, then after a while there
was stillness. She imagined him lying in bed, just
a few feet away from her, and she had to resist a
wish to open the door and watch him as he slept.
It would have been one more memory to add to
all the others.

She loved Clint—she knew that now. What she
had been trying so hard to fight was not mere physical attraction, though that existed in full measure.
She loved Clint, the man. And he would never know
it.

When the project was finished she would go back
to Johannesburg, where Simon would be waiting
for her. She could only hope that he would never
guess that she had left her heart at Devil's View.
That much she owed him. As for Clint, he would
find a new secretary, and there would be his marriage to Miranda. Jana would fade from his memory.

Now and then in the next few days Clint spoke
of the project. It seemed that ways of treating dis-
eases which attacked the grapes had been important
to him for some time. The first time he broached
the subject Jana rose to fetch her notebook, but he
put out a hand to restrain her. He did not need

notes taken. He was organising his thoughts, speaking aloud. And Jana was a willing listener. Working so closely with Clint had given her a deep interest in the wine industry. At Devil's View she would wander sometimes through the vineyards. Looking at the clusters of grapes as they clung to the vines, she would marvel at the processes which turned the fruit into table wines which were among the best in the world.

The last few days had given her a new perspective on Clint as well. If she had ever thought him a rich gentleman farmer, glorying in the luscious beauty of his estate but not involved in the sheer hard work, she now knew different. Never had she dreamed that he was quite so dedicated.

Now and then when he talked she had visions of what it would be like to work with him always. To help him with research, to find new ways of increasing production, perhaps to find new and even more delectable wines. But that thought led always to the other one; working with Clint, living at Devil's View, would be sheer agony if he was married to Miranda. Not that the issue was in question, for Miranda, once married to Clint, would make quite certain that Jana was dispensed with.

They left Hermanus shortly before sunset on Sunday. As she watched Clint lock the cottage and carry the suitcases to the car, she felt as if a part of her was dying. And yet, despite the pain, she had no more regrets at having accompanied him on this week-end. The three days together had been a small island of sheer happiness in which only two people had existed. Nothing else had intruded. There had been no Simon, no Miranda. No telephone, no duties. No extraneous influences of any kind.

Clint came round to her side of the car and opened the door. As if he guessed something of her thoughts, he touched her cheek in a brief caress. 'Perhaps we'll come again some week-end.' There was a smile in the dark eyes, and his voice was unexpectedly gentle.

She nodded, lowering her lids to hide the sudden rush of tears. As the car began to cover the miles back to Cape Town she turned her head away from Clint and looked determinedly out of the window. But this time she was blind to the beauty all around her. There was only the hard knot of pain at the back of her throat. She would never return to the cottage by the sea. Next time Clint came here, he would be with Miranda.

# CHAPTER NINE

MIRANDA arrived at Devil's View soon after their return—an angry Miranda. With Clint she was over-vivacious; laughing and provocative and flirtatious. With Jana, when they were alone together for a few moments, she was venomous. She seemed to have cast Jana in the light of a seductress, implying that she had lured Clint to the cottage, and reiterating that he belonged to her and that she would allow nobody to interfere with their marriage. Jana was silent before the vituperative outburst, too sickened to reply. She was almost relieved when Clint and Miranda vanished in the girl's car.

But all thoughts of Miranda were swept away when she learned from the housekeeper that a man had phoned for her—a Mr Lesands. He had left a Cape Town telephone number and the name of the hotel where he could be contacted.

Simon in Cape Town! With fingers that shook Jana dialled the number. What new complication was about to be added to her life?

'Jana!' He sounded indignant and impatient and not at all loverlike. 'Where the hell have you been?'

'The extra seconds don't count, Simon.' She tried to keep the resentment from her voice.

'I don't understand. . . .'

'Since this is a local call it won't cost extra if you start just for once by telling me that you've missed me.'

'All that stuff again!'

'All that stuff,' she agreed brightly, wondering how it was possible to remain so detached.

Something in her tone must have reached him, for when he spoke again there was a note of uncertainty in his own voice. 'Of course I've missed you, Jana honey. But I take that as understood.'

'I don't.'

There was a moment of silence. As if he was in the room with her, she could see Simon frowning into the mouthpiece, puzzled that Jana, normally compliant and eager to please, was behaving more and more out of character.

Then he said, 'Wait till you see me. My kisses will leave you in no doubt.' His voice grew a little husky. 'I can't wait.'

But *she* could wait, Jana realised with a pang. She would have to be a good actress if she wanted Simon to think she was happy to see him. The thought of his kisses filled her with dismay. There was only one man whose kisses she craved—but that man was not for her. She would have to submit to Simon's lovemaking. More, she would have to learn to enjoy it once more. Unless, of course, she meant to break off her engagement.

There had been moments during the past few days when it had occurred to her to do just that. But on the return to Devil's View there had been the encounter with Miranda. If Clint was going to lead a normal married life, would Jana not be punishing herself unreasonably if she spent the rest of her days alone nursing a broken heart? She would never forget Clint, but marriage would bring its compensations. A husband whom she liked, even if she did not love him as much as she had once thought. A home, children. . . .

'I'm coming to see you.'

'No,' she said a little too quickly. 'No, Simon.'

'Why not?' he asked incredulously. 'Why do you think I came to Cape Town?'

'Yes, I know. . . .' She was stammering, confused by the implications of a visit by Simon to Devil's View. The ring. . . . She looked down at her bare finger. He would expect to see it, and if Clint came upon them there would have to be explanations. But it was more than just the ring. . . . She had never mentioned a fiancé, or that she had come here from Johannesburg.

'I'll meet you in Sea Point,' she told him, as firmly as she was able. 'There's a pretty place on the seafront.' She gave him directions, and told him she would meet him in half an hour, then she put down the receiver before he could raise fresh complications.

There was just time to take a shower and change into a clean sundress. Clint would not miss her, she thought, as she slipped out of the house and walked quickly to the garage and the small borrowed Mini. Even if he did, it was Sunday, and now that they were back at Devil's View what remained of the day was her own.

As she drove down the steep mountain road her eyes kept going to the ring on her fourth left finger. When she had begun to work for Clint and had stopped wearing the ring, her hand had looked bare. Now it was the ring which looked strange, almost as if it had no right to be there....

Simon was waiting for her when she came into the restaurant. He rose from the table and drew her to him. His kiss was brief—there were people at other tables and Simon was always conscious of the proprieties—yet for all its briefness Jana found she had to steel herself to relax. It did not augur well for the future, she thought unhappily.

'Let me look at you, honey,' Simon said, when he had given their order. He studied her with a frown. 'You've changed.'

'Have I?'

'You're thinner, and more tanned. And there's something in your eyes ... I'm not sure what, but it wasn't there before.'

'You're imagining things,' she told him lightly, at the same time marvelling at his perception. For her own part, she too was seeing Simon with new eyes. He was smaller than she had remembered—or was it merely that she had become accustomed to Clint's towering height? And his face seemed a bit sallow. Just a normal Highveld pallor, she remembered. Away from the beaches and the sun, there was no reason why Simon should have the tanned appearance of the Capetonians. Besides, as a rising young executive he was cloistered in an office all day, with only the week-ends for outdoor relaxation. What of the primness in his expression? Had it always been there? And the laughter lines that should be engraved in two curves from his nostrils to his mouth—where were those? Stop comparing, she childed herself. It isn't fair! Simon is not Clint and never will be, but then neither does Clint have Simon's better qualities.

She began to ask him questions. Had he had a good flight, and how was his mother, and what news was there of the office? Her voice was high and her words came too quickly, and she hardly heard his responses as her mind raced ahead in search of other questions. Somehow it seemed important to talk about trivialities for as long as possible. She did not notice that his answers were brief and slightly abstracted. She did not hear what he said. All that mattered was that there should be no silence.

When he reached for her hand, she stopped in mid-sentence. 'You *have* changed,' he said, and there was a note in his voice which she had not heard before. 'Don't you want to know why I came, Jana?'

'To bring me back?' she asked uncertainly. 'Simon, I told you I can't. . . .'

'I know what you told me,' he was belligerent, 'but I don't accept it. I've come to find out the truth for myself.'

The truth.... How would he take the real truth?

'What hold does this man have over you? This Clint Dubois?'

The greatest hold a man can have over a woman; he has all my love. Aloud she said, 'No hold, Simon.'

'Then why did you refuse to come back to Jo'-burg?'

'The project....'

'He could have got someone else in to do it. Nobody is indispensable.'

'I gave him my promise.' Her voice was soft and she felt close to tears, yet defiant with it. 'This project is important, Simon.'

'To you too, Jana?'

'Yes.'

'More important to you than I am?'

The question was asked deliberately and with meaning. She lifted her head and looked at him. His eyes were stormy, but whereas Clint was magnificent when he was angry, Simon had the look of a thwarted child. I must stop comparing, Jana thought.

She did not respond to his question directly. A truthful answer would hurt him, and he did not deserve it. 'I owe Clint some loyalty,' she said quietly.

'So it's Clint, is it?' She saw his nostrils flare, and two spots of colour appeared in his cheeks. 'You *have* got to know him well. Enjoy living in his house, Jana?'

There was an insinuation in his words which

she resented. Forgetting her resolve to be tactful, she said defiantly, 'I told you the terms of my employment before I accepted the job.'

'I didn't like them,' he muttered.

'But you didn't tell me to pack up and come home. In fact,' she leaned forward, green eyes sparkling, 'you wanted me to go on. It was your idea that I make a search, Simon.'

'That's true.' He moved uneasily in his chair. 'You still haven't found it, Jana?'

'No.'

'You've searched the whole house?'

'No.' It was Jana's turn to feel guilt. True, the house was big, and its panelled walls made the search difficult. But she knew that after the first few days her heart had not been seriously in it.

His face brightened. 'Then you could still find it?'

For a long moment she looked at him and wondered what went on in the mind of the man to whom she was engaged. He wanted her to come back to Johannesburg, presumably because he loved her and wanted their marriage to go ahead. But he also wanted the piece of paper she had come to Cape Town to find. Not for the first time she wondered what would have happened if she had refused, from the start, to go to Devil's View to find the clue which Simon deemed so important to their future happiness.

She took a deep breath. Then she said, 'There's still a slight chance, I suppose....'

Perhaps Simon saw the mutinous set of her chin, and was uneasy, for he turned her hand, lifted it and pressed his lips to the palm. 'Jana, I love you, honey. And you love me.... '

'Well, if this isn't romantic!' interrupted a familiar voice.

Simon's words trailed away as he looked at the girl who had interrupted him. He glanced at Jana for enlightment, but none was forthcoming. The colour had drained from her cheeks, and she was gazing in horror at the pretty dark-haired girl and the man who stood a pace or two behind her.

'We *have* interrupted something.' Miranda's voice was sugary with glee. Without warning she bent and dragged up Jana's free left hand for her companion's inspection. 'Clint darling, it looks as if you're about to lose a secretary.'

As she pulled her hand away from Miranda, Jana had eyes only for Clint. He looked more grim than she had ever seen him. There was a whiteness around his jaw and his nostrils, and his eyes, those eyes which so recently had sparkled with warmth and humanity, were chips of grey ice.

'Congratulations seem to be in order.' Miranda was prattling on in the sugary tone which set every one of Jana's nerves on edge. 'You haven't introduced us to your fiancé, Miss Harvey.'

Jana struggled to force words out of a throat which was suddenly quite dry. 'This is Simon Lesands. Simon ... I want you to meet Miss Maddison and Mr Dubois.'

Jana had never imagined that she would ever be glad of Miranda's coy flirtatiousness, but for once the dark-haired girl's shrill remarks filled an awkward silence. Having made the introductions Jana found her throat had dried up so completely that she could not have spoken. As for the two men, neither one seemed to feel that politeness called for speech. Simon was regarding Clint with an unfeigned hostility to which was added astonishment. It was obvious, Jana thought wryly, that Simon's mental picture of her employer had not prepared him in any way for this arrogantly handsome stranger. Clint looked tall and unbending. His eyes rested with distaste on the younger man's red-faced hostility. Then, as if what he saw bored him, he removed his gaze to another point in the room while he waited for Miranda to end her babbling.

That girl was making as much out of the engagement, Jana thought wryly, as if she had never seen an engaged couple before. 'Are we the first to congratulate you?' she asked in the gushing tone which made Jana feel ill.

'Yes,' said Jana.

'No,' said Simon.

'Well, which is it?' Miranda asked curiously.

'We became engaged some time ago.' Simon sounded stiff and angry. 'You must have noticed Jana's ring.'

Jana held her breath. She was unable to speak. Nothing she could say now would save the situation. She stole a glance at Clint, searching his face for a sign of emotion, but his face was without expression. There was just the iciness in his eyes, and the angry whiteness she had glimpsed before, and a look of sheer boredom which appalled Jana more than anger would have done.

Miranda's brittle laugh splintered the taut silence. She addressed herself to Clint. 'I think we would have noticed the ring if Miss Harvey had been wearing it, wouldn't we, darling?'

Clint's shrug was one of unconcern. 'You said you were hungry, Miranda. Let's get to our table.'

'Whatever you say, darling.' Miranda pouted up at him, then turned to Jana with a triumphant expression. 'Wretched man! He's so deliciously cave-man, isn't he?' Blue eyes shot a dazzling look at Simon. 'So *nice* to have met you, Mr Lesands.'

Jana watched them walk away, Clint's long lean form straight and rigid, Miranda's hand tucked possessively through his arm. Jana felt drained, numb. More than anything she wanted to get back to her room, to close the door and throw herself on to her bed, to sob until there was not a tear left in her eyes.

'Jana....'

Incredibly, for a few moments she had forgotten Simon's presence. Slowly she looked up at him, and wondered if he saw the pain in her eyes.

'You haven't been wearing your ring?'

'No.'

'Why not?' His face was flushed with anger. 'Did

you think you stood a better shot at your boss without it?'

'No,' she said quietly. Simon's challenge deserved a stinging retaliation. But she was tired, so very tired. And it no longer seemed to matter what her fiancé thought. 'It's true that I haven't worn the ring. I thought I'd have a better chance of getting into Devil's View without it.'

'I'd like to believe you. . . .' Simon looked at her uncertainly, as if he did not understand this new Jana, who answered him so quietly, and who did not seem to care how he took her words.

She shrugged; it was less effort than speaking.

'Is Clint Dubois engaged to Miss Maddison?'

'It would seem so.' The words came painfully. 'At least, unofficially.'

'Then—there couldn't be anything between the two of you?'

'What are you trying to say, Simon?'

'Just that, if there's nothing between you, perhaps you should go on with the search a while longer.' He caught the look in Jana's eyes, correctly gauged her disbelief and contempt, and two bright spots of angry red appeared in his face. 'Dammit, Jana, can't you say anything?'

'What do you mean by "a while longer"?' she asked carefully.

'Till the project is finished.' His voice was steadier now, he seemed more sure of himself. 'You seem to feel you owe the fellow some loyalty.

In a way I can understand that. It's one of the things I love you for.' Again he kissed her hand. I feel nothing, Jana thought. Nothing.

'Tell me, Simon,' she asked curiously, 'if I do find the paper and it doesn't come up to expectation, what then?'

'Please, Jana. . . .' He was uneasy.

'Would you still want to marry me?' she persisted.

The eyes which rested on her face a moment were angry and confused, as if Simon found it hard to know how to deal with her in her unaccustomed mood. Then his gaze shifted away from her. 'Why discuss an eventuality that's purely hypothetical?'

He had deliberately evaded the question, and in doing so had given her an answer. Did he know it? Jana wondered.

They stayed a while longer in the restaurant. Simon explained that he had business in Cape Town, and that he would be some time in the city. Probably by the time he had to return to Johannesburg Jana would have finished typing the project, and they could travel back together. They began to talk of other things, of people and happenings in Johannesburg, but the conversation was forced. They were like two strangers, seeking for topics in order to avoid a silence which would be awkward. Jana tried to respond, she smiled at weak jokes, but all the while she was more aware of the couple who sat in a dim corner of the restaurant than of the man at her own table.

After a while they left the restaurant and walked for a while along the promenade. Jana was glad of the people who spilled from the apartments and hotels of Sea Front to enjoy the salty evening freshness. What with the noise of the sea and the buzz of chatter all around them, Simon seemed content to be silent.

Her head was aching when she left him at last and began the drive back to Devil's View. Except for the light on the verandah, the house appeared to be in almost total darkness. Clint must have got back some time ago, she thought with relief. In a few minutes she would be in her room and she would be able to give way to the tears which had been threatening all evening.

As silently as she could she passed his room. Not a sound. He must be asleep. She was halfway into her own room when she saw the long lean shape in the chair beside her bed, and she thought her heart would stop.

'Clint!' she whispered, clapping a hand to her mouth.

'A fine time to come home,' he observed as he rose from the chair in a swiftly fluid movement. In the dark he looked like some predator of the night, sleek and dangerous and ready to attack.

'I'm not accountable to you for the time I get in,' she retaliated. 'Get out of my room!'

'This is my house,' he told her coldly.

'Next thing you'll be telling me this bed is yours, too,' she said wildly.

'If you're trying to seduce me you're wasting your time,' he said with icy distaste. 'I take my pleasure when *I* want it.'

'Then why are you here?'

'Because I want an explanation.'

'Can't it wait till the morning?' Her tone had lost some of its defiance. She sounded vulnerable and uncertain.

'To give you more time to think up some farcical story? No, Jana, you'll talk now.'

'I'm so tired,' she pleaded, pressing a hand against an aching temple.

'Start talking, then you can go to bed,' was the unsympathetic answer.

'You don't care how I feel.....'

'Not in the least.' His tone was so cold, so dispassionate, that she knew he meant every word.

She looked at him, tall and lithe and so devastatingly sensuous that even through her tiredness she could feel her senses reacting to his presence in her room. A shudder passed through her. It was not fair, she thought despairingly, that a man should have it in his power to move another person quite so much.

'You want to know about Simon. And I don't know where to begin....'

'Why not at the beginning?' he asked mockingly. 'I want to hear every sordid detail.'

'It's not sordid!' she flung at him.

'No? Perhaps we have a different set of values. You came into my house under false pretences. You must have been engaged to Simon even then.'

He looked at her for confirmation, and she nodded.

'You weren't wearing a ring. You didn't wear it when you came for the interview. You haven't worn it all the time you've lived here. You weren't even wearing it that day at Fish Hoek, when you tricked me into rescuing you and pretended. . . .'

'I did not trick you!' she interrupted him furiously. 'I've told you often enough that I was caught in a whirlpool.'

He was silent a moment. When he spoke again there was no apology in his tone. 'Assuming you're telling the truth about that, it still leaves us with the fact that you've been hiding your engagement all this time.'

'Yes. . . .' she acknowledged unhappily.

'Why?' A single step breached the distance between them. The hands that gripped her shoulders were hard and strong. 'You were so determined to work for me. You must have had a damn good reason, Jana.'

She tried to pull away from him, but his grip was unrelenting. He was so close to her that her nostrils were filled with the overpowering smell of his maleness. It was difficult to breathe, to think. But she must try. The uncompromising set of his face told her that he would not leave her alone till she had told him what he wanted to know.

'I had a reason,' she said at last. 'But it had nothing to do with you, Clint.' She lifted her chin. 'I told you once before that I didn't come to steal your silver.'

'Not the silver, perhaps. But something else.'

'Something that belonged to me,' she acknowledged quietly. 'And it wasn't a case of stealing.'

He was silent while he studied her, taking in the proud lift of the chin, the eyes that held the sparkle of anger, the quiver of soft lips. His stance lost none of its rigidity, but his voice softened slightly. 'Care to tell me about it?'

Her gaze met his for a long moment. She would tell him, of course; she should have told him at the start. It was only fear of his ridicule which had kept her silent. She was aware of the dull pain in her chest. For a while, during the enchantment of the days at the fishing cottage, she had thought that a new dimension had been added to their relationship; that even when he was married to Miranda he would remember Jana with fondness and affection. But with the telling of the story all that would be left would be contempt and perhaps pity. Maybe it was all she deserved; for some time now she had despised herself for agreeing to Simon's wishes.

'Let me go first,' she said simply.

He released her chin and she stood a few paces away from him.

'I spent the first four years of my life at Devil's View,' she began slowly, and saw that the words brought a gleam of surprise to the dark eyes. She faltered slightly. Then she turned resolutely to the window, and did not look at Clint again until she had finished her story.

She had been an adopted child, she told him, brought to Devil's View in the first week of her life. Her adoptive parents were the only ones she had ever known, and she had loved them very much. Nevertheless, there had been times when she had enjoyed fantasising, when she had wondered about her real parents, and had spun dreams about her origins. Her grandmother had lived with them, both at Devil's View and later in Johannesburg, the city to which they had moved when her father had given up mine-making. It was her grandmother who had been the recipient of a little girl's fantasies, and it was she who had said that the truth of Jana's birth was every bit as fine as her dreams, that her real parents were people of whom she would have been proud.

'She never told me details,' said Jana, her eyes on the moving clouds in the dark sky beyond her window, 'but from the way she talked I gathered that my parents had been very special people, and that only circumstances had made it impossible for them to keep me.'

The old lady had remained stubborn in the face of all Jana's questions. She had refused to tell her more than she already knew. But when she was old and very frail and knew that she was dying she had told Jana of a paper. The paper was somewhere at Devil's View, and in it were details of Jana's birth.

The old lady had exacted a promise. Jana should not unearth her identity on a whim. If she decided to go to Devil's View to find the paper, it must be only because she had a real need to know more about herself. In any event, she must not undertake a search before she was either twenty-one or about to get married. It had not occurred to Jana to ask where exactly the paper was hidden. She had got over her childish dreams long ago. She loved her adoptive parents, and was content with life.

It was after the motor-accident in which her parents were killed that she met Simon. Soon they were spending more and more of their time together. Jana had been sad and lonely, shattered by the double loss, and Simon had filled a gap. He had been sympathetic and kind, gentle and understanding. She could not remember an actual proposal on his part—somehow it had been taken for granted that they would be married.

She was silent a few moments. Then she said, 'It was after Simon had given me the ring and the engagement was formally announced that he said I should come here and find the clue to my origins.'

It seemed that as the future wife of Simon Lesands, rising star in the big company started by his parents, she had spoken too freely of her babyhood. She had not realised the embarrassment caused to her fiancé and his mother.... The redeeming feature was the fact that her grandmother had always hinted at noble origins. If she could find the secret, and if Simon's mother could speak of them with pride, then she would be welcome in the Lesands family.

'If you don't find it?' They were Cliff's first words since she had begun speaking. She looked at him, seeking for some reaction to her story, but his face was in shadow and his tone was too expressionless to be revealing.

'I ... don't know.'

'Simon would ask for his ring back?'

'I think I would feel impelled to give it to him.' Her voice shook slightly. 'I couldn't become a member of his family, knowing that they were ashamed of me.'

# CHAPTER TEN

THERE was a short silence. Jana was intensely aware of Clint's presence. Just a few days ago they had been alone together in the cottage beside the sea. Then there had been only happiness. She remembered the swirl of the waves about their bodies, and the intimacy of their meals beneath the stars. She remembered their walks on the beach, and the fingers stroking sun-tan oil into her back. She had thought the memories would bring only pleasure, but now they brought pain—because the experiences would never be repeated.

'Why didn't you tell me the truth at the start?' he demanded, and now his tone was harsh.

'I thought ... you'd think me ridiculous,' she whispered.

'Damn right! I would have!' His voice was like ice. 'I thought you had some backbone, Jana. Now I'm beginning to wonder.'

'Because I agreed to the search?' And when he nodded: 'At the time it seemed I had no alternative.'

'No alternative!' He ground out the words. 'You're an able-bodied girl. You're brave and independent. I can see no reason why you should have to cater to the whims of a slob.'

'Simon is not a slob!' For some reason she felt she must defend him.

'A slob and a snob,' Clint said contemptuously. He crossed the gap between them and once more she felt his hands grip her shoulders. 'And a darn fool.'

'A fool?' came the disbelieving question.

'A man who requires a pedigree to know what you are, Jana Harvey, is a fool.' The grip hardened. 'And what about you? You'd be prepared to spend the rest of your life with him?'

If I can't spend it with you, what does it matter whom I marry? Aloud she said, 'Yes.'

'He's rich?'

'He isn't poor,' Jana said indifferently.

'Riches and social status. For those two qualities you're prepared to prostitute yourself.' Clint's voice was thick with contempt.

Jana felt anger churning inside her. Clint's arrogance was undeserved. 'At least Simon is polite and a gentleman,' she threw at him.

'And you think his politeness will keep you satisfied in bed? Don't kid yourself, Jana. You'll be unfaithful to him a month after your marriage.'

'How dare you!' she spat at him.

'Like this, my little wildcat,' he told her, as he pulled her to him.

There was no chance to escape. She knew already that he was stronger than she was. His hands pressed against her back pulling her against him, moulding her soft femininity to his uncompromising maleness. The lips that covered hers were hard and punishing, exploring and tasting and probing with a possessiveness that made her dizzy. One hand went to her zipper and pulled it down, then caressed her back a moment before curling round to find the softness of a breast. Flames of pleasure shot through her. There was no thought now, no resentment. Now she was wholly a woman in the arms of the man she loved, wanting only to yield to him, to be possessed by him. Instinctively she put her arms around his neck and pressed herself even closer.

When he pushed her away from him she could only stare at him through pain-numbed eyes. Had he known how close she was to giving in to him? That there was nothing she would not have let him do? One look at the contempt in the taut chiselled mask told her that he did know. He knew that she would have let him make love to her fully, just as he knew that he had shaken her to the very depths of her being. A little desperately she searched his face for any sign of emotion, any indication that he too had been moved. His breathing was a little ragged, but otherwise there was nothing to show that his lovemaking had meant to him anything more than proof of his accusation.

'Please go,' she said shakily.

'That was my intention.' His tone was bland.

He reached the door when she said, 'Clint. . . .'

He paused, and turned his head to look at her.

'Do you ... do you still want me to go on with the project?'

The strong lips curved in a mirthless smile. 'Of course. This little—exercise—hasn't changed that part of our relationship.'

Jana began to type the next morning. Clint gave her the sheaf of handwritten papers, and in a matter-of-fact way explained what he wanted her to do. There was no reference to what had happened between them; it was as if the affair had been erased from his memory. Now he was solely Clint Dubois, master of one of the greatest wine estates in the Cape, with a big and important research project which must be completed.

In a way Jana was thankful for his impersonal manner. Though it hurt her to see him behave towards her as if she was nothing more than an employee, it made working with him bearable. She must resign herself to the fact that he felt nothing for her, and that his kisses were no more than a normal male's desire to enjoy an available girl. She wondered what Miranda would make of those kisses. For a man who was engaged to be married, Clint was not demonstrating the qualities of a faithful husband-to-be. Miranda, Jana thought with a certain amount of pity, would have difficulties of her own when she was mistress of Devil's View.

The days passed, and a routine was established. Jana wondered sometimes if the routine seemed peculiar only to herself. Every morning she worked with Clint in an atmosphere that was clinical and impersonal—at least as far as Clint was concerned. In the evenings there was Simon. He was still in the city, occupied with the affairs of the firm's Cape Town branch. There was also Miranda. Since the week-end at the fishing-cottage the girl made almost daily appearances at Devil's View, but her presence did not affect Jana as much as it once had. She was growing accustomed to the girl's venom.

Now and then the four of them spent an evening together; Clint and Miranda, Jana and Simon. If Clint still despised Simon, Jana thought she was the only one present who sensed his feelings. Outwardly Clint was polite, almost friendly—which, in some way, made his contempt more intense. Between Simon and Miranda there was a natural affinity. Simon was visibly impressed by the pretty brunette with her impeccable lineage, and Miranda played up to him, flirting with him, teasing him, asking endless questions about his work and his position. Jana was an unconcerned onlooker. Now and then she would find Clint watching her appraisingly. Perhaps he wondered that she was able to accept the situation with such good grace. He did not know that Simon's attentions to Miranda meant nothing to her. A nothingness which was so complete that this in itself should have been a cause for disquiet.

And perhaps it would have been, if her mind had not been so taken up with Clint. Her mind, her heart, all her being. She loved Clint so much that she wondered sometimes that her feelings were not outwardly apparent for all to see. She passed her days in a kind of blank unhappiness, and out of that feeling came a new thought, an alternative she had never considered before.

Till now she had taken it for granted that she would marry Simon—in the event that he still wanted her—because if she could not have Clint it did not matter whom she married. Only gradually did it dawn on her that there was a certain shame in waiting to see if Simon still wanted her; that it was wrong to marry a man whom she did not love, purely because it was the sensible thing to do. On that dreadful night when Clint had set out to prove to her that she was prostituting herself, he had called her brave and independent. Perhaps it was true. If she could work for a person as demanding and impatient as Clint Dubois she could work for anyone.

Out of these thoughts was born a new knowledge of herself and of what she should be doing. She did not love Simon. It was an error to think that marriage would breed its own kind of love—it would not. She did love Clint. Perhaps she would always love him. But there was no future with Clint. It could be only a matter of time now before he was married to Miranda.

She would have to tell Simon that she could not marry him. And when the project was finished, as it would be very soon now, she would begin a new life. She would remain in Cape Town. Once she had thought she could not live in the same city as Clint and Miranda, but when she considered the matter reasonably the odds were not great that she would meet them together. And the beautiful city had taken its hold of her. Perhaps, she thought wryly, she might even end up going more deeply into the subject of Cape Dutch architecture. . . .

But all that lay in the future. For the present there was the need to talk to Simon. There was also a new need, the urge to find out more about herself. And the clue to that lay within the walls of Devil's View.

Until now her search had been half-hearted, almost as if she had not wanted to find the piece of paper of which her grandmother had told her.

Now she plunged herself into the search with fresh vigour. She no longer waited for Clint to be out of the way. He was aware of her reasons for being at Devil's View, and if he was contemptuous, that was nothing new. She steeled herself to live with that contempt.

She was nearing the end of the project when Miranda came for lunch. The other girl was looking exceptionally pretty. In her few moments alone with Jana she was her usual nasty self, but a new dimension had been added. This time she was also harping on her prowess with Simon. With Clint she was flirtatious, laughing and scintillating. Watching him respond to her overtures, Jana withdrew into herself. Only when she was spoken to, and that was rarely, did she speak.

After lunch she watched Clint and Miranda go off together. Despondently she went to her office and sat down at her desk. For a while she typed, but her mind was not on her work and the pages were filled with errors. Presently she pushed the typewriter from her. Clint was a perfectionist, and her work today was unacceptable; she would give it a break. He was with Miranda and would not know that Jana had left her desk.

She thought of taking the car and driving to one of the beaches. She was on her way to the garage with her bikini and her towel when she changed her mind. In her depressed mood she would not enjoy the waves.

She would continue the search. Soon now the project would be finished and she would leave Devil's View. There would never be another chance to learn the truth about herself.

There was only one room which she had left untouched—Clint's bedroom. She had never summoned the courage to search there. If she intended to look in his room, today was the right time. She would be undisturbed.

She had been in this room only once before, and just for a few moments, but even then she had been struck by its atmosphere. Something of Clint's special male aura seemed to linger here; Jana could feel it all around her. On a chair was a shirt he had worn earlier in the day. She picked it up and pressed it to her cheek. When she put it down it was with reluctance. There was so much panelling in this room. If she was going to search, the sooner she got down to it the better. She would start in the corner by the bed.

She was on her knees, her hands pressed to the panelling, when she heard the door open. She spun round, her heart hammering in fright.

'Clint!' The word was a stifled gasp.

'Well, well.' A sardonic drawl. 'How very interesting!'

'I can explain,' she said desperately.

'Honey, a girl in a man's bedroom is sufficient explanation.' There was an unholy light in the dark eyes as he strode towards her.

'No, Clint, I....'

She wanted to tell him her motive for being in his room, but his mouth closed on hers before she could finish the sentence. His arms were around her back, and she felt herself being pushed back towards the bed. With the delicious agony his touch always provoked, there was also fear. She had no resources of strength left with which to defend herself—if, indeed, she had ever had any resources where Clint was concerned. If he tried to make her his she would not be able to fight him, for she would have to fight herself first and she knew she could not do it. She must get away from him now, before it was too late. If Clint had his way she would have one more memory to carry with her always, and it was a memory which would haunt her to the end of her days.

From somewhere she found the strength to push away from him. She heard his exclamation of anger, and then he was reaching for her again. She stepped backwards, and in the next moment her foot had caught at a dresser. Clint pulled her from its path as it fell, the drawers spilling on to the floor.

There was a taut silence between them as they picked up the drawers. Clint did not try to touch her again. It was as if, for the moment, he was giving her time to calm herself. In a way Jana was glad of the mess on the floor; it gave them something to do.

Later she was to wonder what made her spot the tiny indentation at the back of the bottom drawer. On impulse she pressed a finger against it. There was a smooth sliding sound, and a moment later a tiny cavity was revealed. At the bottom of the cavity lay a piece of paper. Jana heard Clint's swift intake of breath as she reached for the paper.

'Jana.' His hand was on hers. 'Certain you want to look at it?'

The eyes she raised to his were green and steady. 'I think I must.'

Very slowly she opened the folded paper. Twice she read what was written. Then, without a word, she handed the paper to Clint. While he read it she went to stand at the window, to look out at the garden and the vineyards in the valley beyond.

The fine copperplate writing had been that of

her grandmother, and the message had been in the form of a letter to Jana. For the first time she learned that her real mother had been the goddaughter of her grandparents, a lovely young girl of seventeen who had fallen in love with a student of music and had found that she was carrying his child. It appeared that Jana's father had been a gifted young man, a pianist on the threshold of a promising career, and the girl had not wanted to spoil things for him by forcing him into marriage before he was ready for it. She had died a week after giving birth to her baby, and the child, Jana, had been adopted by the daughter of the grandmother, the woman whom Jana had always looked upon as her mother.

'Why am I telling you all this, my darling Jana?' her grandmother had written. 'Not because I want you ever to think of your adoptive parents as anything but your own—they brought you up with all the love and care any child could want. But there may be times in your life when you will wonder about your true origins. Don't look with scorn upon the girl who gave you birth. She was very lovely, good and pure and beautiful. Be proud of her, Jana, and if you think of her, let it be with the love that she deserves.'

'Jana?' Clint was behind her. Two hands turned her gently round to face him. 'Sorry you found it?'

'Oh, no!' Her expression was radiant. 'I'm glad.'

'Simon won't like it.' Grey eyes were steady, questioning.

'No.' She could not tell him that in a way she was glad. That it would make it easier for her to do what she must.

'He's here, Jana.' There was a slight lift at the corner of his mouth. 'He arrived just when I did. You weren't in the office. He's waiting in the library.'

'He's in the library?' And when Clint nodded, 'Then I'll go there now.'

Clint did not ask if she would show Simon the letter she had come so far to find. Perhaps he did not care.

Simon sat restlessly on a chair in the library. Jana saw him before he was aware of her presence, and she noted the expression of petulant impatience, and marvelled at how little she had really known him.

'Simon. . . .' she began.

'Jana! Where the devil have you been?' He jumped to his feet and came to her.

'I found something, Simon.'

'The paper?' His voice was eager.

'Yes.' Her voice was low and grave. 'Simon— before you read it, I want to give you this.' She pulled the diamond ring from her finger and put it in his hand.

When he had finished reading the letter he looked at her. His colour was high, and she saw that his eyes were uneasy. 'Jana, you don't have to do this. . . .'

'It's better this way,' she told him steadily.

'Honey, I don't know....' He looked away from her in unhappy embarrassment.

'I do.' And she did. If she had never known it before, she knew it now. For if Simon had loved her, truly loved her, he would have pulled her into his arms and said, 'This piece of paper makes no difference to our lives.'

She was folding clothes and putting them into a suitcase when Clint came into the room.

'You've seen Simon?' he asked without even the preamble of an apology for entering her room without knocking.

'Yes.'

'How did he take it?' The grey eyes were studying her with an intensity which sent the blood racing in her veins.

Carefully she folded a cardigan and placed it neatly in the case. 'I didn't wait to find out. I gave him back his ring first.' There was just the slightest suggestion of a tremor in her voice. 'Cowardice, I expect.'

'You were never a coward in your life.' His eyes went to the clothes on her bed. 'What are you doing?'

'Packing.'

The dark eyebrows lifted. 'Going somewhere?'

She could not meet the steady gaze. 'The project will be finished soon. Then ... you'll have no further use for me.'

'Not as a typist perhaps.' There was a bubble

of laughter in his throat. 'Empty the case, Jana. You're not leaving.'

'Clint?' She looked up at him, hope surging inside her. 'You ... you've other work for me?'

'Wifely work.' His arms went around her, and she felt the steady beat of his heart against her chest. 'Let me hear you say yes, my darling.'

Happiness flooded through her such as she had never known. Yet still she could not believe it. Leaning back a little so that she could look into the face of the man she loved more than life, she asked, 'What about Miranda?'

'I think she'll be quite happy with your Simon.' Laughter once more, the sound of it low and vibrantly sensuous. 'He did me a favour coming here when he did. Miranda was becoming too much of a nuisance.'

'You mean you never....' It was still hard for her to grasp. 'Clint, the innkeeper said you didn't like women....'

'I'd only met girls like Miranda till you came along.' His eyes were serious now. 'Girls who were out for money and status. I was nearly trapped once, and I swore it would never happen again.'

'Clint....' Still she could not take it in. 'Clint, do you ...? I mean....'

'You want me to say it? Yes, my darling, I love you. I've loved you since the day you set foot in Devil's View.'

'You knew I was after something.' She nestled her head in the warm throbbing hollow of his throat.

'Why didn't you send me away?'

'Because I'd have lost you.' He held her a little away from him. 'I have to know, my darling. You're not coming to me on the rebound?'

She laughed, and there was a tiny sob in her voice. 'I haven't wanted Simon for a long time. Oh, Clint, it's been such hell! Loving you since the day you rescued me, and thinking you didn't want me. I still can't believe this is true.'

'Well, you'd better begin to believe it. Because as soon as it can be arranged you're going to be my wife.' His lips met hers in a kiss that held all the warmth and tenderness that she had suspected was in him. 'Welcome, my dearest love. This is your real return to Devil's View.'

# Titles available this month in the Mills & Boon ROMANCE Series

**RETURN TO DEVIL'S VIEW** *by Rosemary Carter*
Jana could only succeed in her search for some vital information by working as secretary to the enigmatic Clint Dubois — and it was clear that Clint suspected her motives . . .

**THE MAN ON THE PEAK** *by Katrina Britt*
The last thing Suzanne had wanted or expected when she went to Hong Kong for a holiday was to run into her ex-husband Raoul . . .

**TOGETHER AGAIN** *by Flora Kidd*
Ellen and Dermid Craig had separated, but now circumstances had brought Ellen back to confront Dermid again. Was this her chance to rebuild her marriage, or was it too late?

**A ROSE FROM LUCIFER** *by Anne Hampson*
Colette had always loved the imposing Greek Luke Marlis, but only now was he showing that he was interested in her. Interested — but not, it seemed, enough to want to marry her . . .

**THE JUDAS TRAP** *by Anne Mather*
When Sara Fortune fell in love with Michael Tregower, and he with her, all could have ended happily. Had it not been for the secret that Sara dared not tell him . . .

**THE TEMPESTUOUS FLAME** *by Carole Mortimer*
Caroline had no intention of marrying Greg Fortnum, whom she didn't even know apart from his dubious reputation — so she escaped to Cumbria where she met the mysterious André . . .

**WITH THIS RING** *by Mary Wibberley*
Siana had no memory of who she really was. But what were Matthew Craven's motives when he appeared and announced that he was going to help her find herself again?

**SOLITAIRE** *by Sara Craven*
The sooner Marty got away from Luc Dumarais the better, for Luc was right out of her league, and to let him become important to her would mean nothing but disaster . . .

**SWEET COMPULSION** *by Victoria Woolf*
Marcy Campion was convinced that she was right not to let Randal Saxton develop her plot of land — if only she could be equally convinced about her true feelings for Randal!

**SHADOW OF THE PAST** *by Robyn Donald*
Morag would have enjoyed going back to Wharuaroa, where she had been happy as a teenager, if it hadn't meant coming into constant contact with Thorpe Cunningham.

## Mills & Boon Romances
*– all that's pleasurable in Romantic Reading!*

**Available September 1979**

# Forthcoming Mills & Boon Romances

**CHATEAU IN THE PALMS** *by Anne Hampson*
Philippe de Chameral could have made Jane happy — but he did not know that she was a married woman . . .

**SAVAGE POSSESSION** *by Margaret Pargeter*
Melissa had been too used to having her own way to allow Ryan Trevelyan to dominate her — but she soon had to change her tune!

**ONE MORE RIVER TO CROSS** *by Essie Summers*
Rebecca was as different from her flighty cousin Becky as chalk from cheese, but the girls' identical appearance was to get Rebecca into a difficult situation with the bossy Darroch . . .

**LURE OF EAGLES** *by Anne Mather*
An unknown cousin had inherited the family business, and Domine found herself agreeing to the masterful Luis Aguilar's suggestion that she accompany him to South America to meet the girl.

**MIDNIGHT SUN'S MAGIC** *by Betty Neels*
Could Annis ever make Jake see that she had married him for love, and not on the rebound?

**LOVE IS A FRENZY** *by Charlotte Lamb*
Seventeen-year-old Nicky Hammond's devotion was touching, but Rachel couldn't possibly return it. Yet how could she convince his disapproving father Mark that she wasn't cradle-snatching — or worse?

**THIS SIDE OF PARADISE** *by Kay Thorpe*
Gina's so-called friend was after a man with money, so Gina couldn't really blame Ryan Barras when he got entirely the wrong idea about her . . .

**A LAND CALLED DESERET** *by Janet Dailey*
LaRaine had always been able to twist men round her finger but, as luck would have it, she fell in love with Travis McCrea — who had no time for her at all!

**TANGLED SHADOWS** *by Flora Kidd*
Kathryn could hardly refuse to return to her husband when she learned from his family that he had lost his memory in an accident — but would he remember what had destroyed the marriage in the first place?

**THE PASSIONATE WINTER** *by Carole Mortimer*
Piers Sinclair was her boy-friend's father: older, more sophisticated, far more experienced than she was. And so of course Leigh fell in love with him . . .

*— all that's pleasurable in Romantic Reading!*
**Available October 1979**

Also available this month
Four titles in our Mills & Boon
Classics Series
*Specially chosen reissues of the best in
Romantic Fiction*

September's Titles are:

### DARK ENEMY
*by Anne Mather*

Determined to revenge herself on Jason Wilde because of the
way he had treated her sister, Nicola took a job with the oil
company Jason worked for. To achieve her purpose, she
determined to make him attracted to her. But things did not
quite work out in the manner she expected.

### MY HEART'S A DANCER
*by Roberta Leigh*

Melanie's marriage had ended before it had begun — but
happily it was not long before she found herself in love once
again. Yet even now happiness looked like eluding her, when
her career as a ballet dancer began to come between her and
the man she loved.

### SECRET HEIRESS
*by Eleanor Farnes*

Young love is a pretty sight; but is it always strong and
durable? Fiona's father had his doubts, and that was why he
arranged for her to see a little of life outside her own small
circle before becoming engaged to Guy. Would the experi-
ment be successful, or might it lead her into real unhappiness?

### THE PAGAN ISLAND
*by Violet Winspear*

In an effort to forget her grief over her beloved Dion's
death, Hebe had gone to the lovely Greek island of Petra.
There she met Nikos Stephanos, a man as different from
Dion as he could possibly be. But a dark tragedy lay over
Nikos's life. Would he bring tragedy to Hebe as well?

**Mills & Boon Classics**
*— all that's great in Romantic Reading!*

**BUY THEM TODAY**

# Forthcoming Classic Romances

### A GIRL ALONE
#### by Lilian Peake

Sparks had flown between Lorraine Ferrers and Alan Darby from the moment they met — and it was all Lorraine's fault, for not trying to conceal her prejudice against him. Then, unwillingly, she found herself falling in love with him — but hadn't she left it a little late?

### JAKE HOWARD'S WIFE
#### by Anne Mather

Jake Howard was immensely attractive, immensely rich, immensely successful. His wife Helen was beautiful, intelligent, well bred. A perfect couple, in fact, and a perfect marriage, everyone said. But everyone was wrong . . .

### A QUESTION OF MARRIAGE
#### by Rachel Lindsay

Beth was brokenhearted when Danny Harding let her down, and vowed that it would be a long time before she fell in love again. But fall in love again she did — with Danny's cousin Dean, a very different type of man indeed, and one who really loved her. Or did he? Surely fate wouldn't be so cruel as to strike Beth again in the same way?

### WHISPERING PALMS
#### by Rosalind Brett

The discovery of mineral deposits on her African farm came just at the right time for Lesley, but besides prosperity, it brought a scheming sister determined to get most of the spoils herself and to marry the most eligible bachelor in Central Africa.

## Mills & Boon Classic Romances

*— all that's best in Romantic Reading*

Available October 1979

Cut-out and post this page to order any of the
popular titles (overleaf) from the exciting **NEW**

Mills & Boon
## Golden Treasury
### COLLECTION

# EXCLUSIVE, DIRECT-DELIVERY OFFER

**BRAND NEW** — Exclusive to regular Mills and Boon readers
only on DIRECT-DELIVERY ORDERS by post! This unique
series brings you the **pick** of our all-time, best-selling romances
by top-favourite authors . . . all newly republished, in a thrilling new format, as the MILLS AND BOON GOLDEN
TREASURY COLLECTION.

See overleaf for details of 10 wonderful titles — all available
NOW at just 50p each! HURRY! Make your selection NOW
and place your DIRECT-DELIVERY ORDER below.

**Post to: MILLS & BOON READER SERVICE,
P.O. Box No. 236, Thornton Road, Croydon,
Surrey CR9 3RU, England**

**Please send me the titles I have ticked ☐ overleaf from
the NEW Mills and Boon Golden Treasury Collection.**

I enclose £..........(No C.O.D.) Please ADD 18p if only ONE
book is ordered. If TWO (or more) are ordered please ADD just
10p *per book*. MAXIMUM CHARGE 60p if SIX (or more) books
are ordered.

**Please write in BLOCK LETTERS below**

**NAME (Mrs/Miss)** ..................................................

**ADDRESS**..................................................

**CITY/TOWN** ..................................................

**POSTAL/ZIP CODE** ..................................................

\* Readers in Australia and New Zealand please note that
these titles are available only through membership of
Romance Book Club, PO Box 958, North Sydney, NSW 2060

*\*South African and Rhodesian readers please write for
local prices to P.O. Box 11190, Johannesburg 2000, S. Africa.*

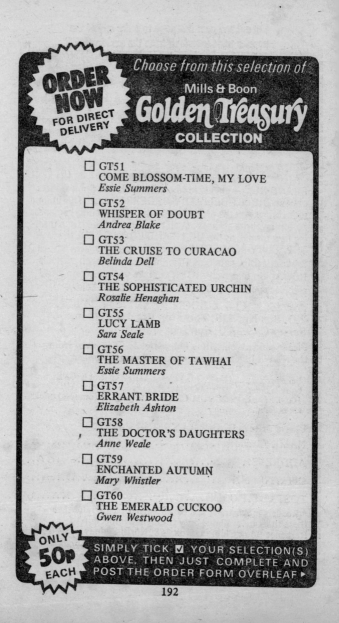

ORDER NOW
FOR DIRECT DELIVERY

Choose from this selection of

Mills & Boon

# Golden Treasury
## COLLECTION

☐ **GT51**
**COME BLOSSOM-TIME, MY LOVE**
*Essie Summers*

☐ **GT52**
**WHISPER OF DOUBT**
*Andrea Blake*

☐ **GT53**
**THE CRUISE TO CURACAO**
*Belinda Dell*

☐ **GT54**
**THE SOPHISTICATED URCHIN**
*Rosalie Henaghan*

☐ **GT55**
**LUCY LAMB**
*Sara Seale*

☐ **GT56**
**THE MASTER OF TAWHAI**
*Essie Summers*

☐ **GT57**
**ERRANT BRIDE**
*Elizabeth Ashton*

☐ **GT58**
**THE DOCTOR'S DAUGHTERS**
*Anne Weale*

☐ **GT59**
**ENCHANTED AUTUMN**
*Mary Whistler*

☐ **GT60**
**THE EMERALD CUCKOO**
*Gwen Westwood*

ONLY **50p** EACH

SIMPLY TICK ☑ YOUR SELECTION(S) ABOVE, THEN JUST COMPLETE AND POST THE ORDER FORM OVERLEAF ▶